TO
THE MOST HIGH,
MIGHTIE
AND
MAGNIFICENT
EMPRESSE RENOVV-
MED FOR PIETIE, VER-
TVE, AND ALL GRATIOVS
GOVERNMENT ELIZABETH BY
THE GRACE OF GOD QVEENE
OF ENGLAND FRAVNCE AND
IRELAND AND OF VIRGIN-
IA, DEFENDOVR OF THE
FAITH, &c. HER MOST
HVMBLE SERVAVNT
EDMVND SPENSER
DOTH IN ALL HV-
MILITIE DEDI-
CATE, PRE-
SENT
AND CONSECRATE THESE
HIS LABOVRS TO LIVE
WITH THE ETERNI-
TIE OF HER
FAME.

SAINT ✳ GEORGE
✳ AND THE ✳
DRAGON

BEING The Legend of the Red Cross Knight
✠ *from* ✠
THE FAERIE QUEENE
✠ BY EDMUND SPENSER ✠

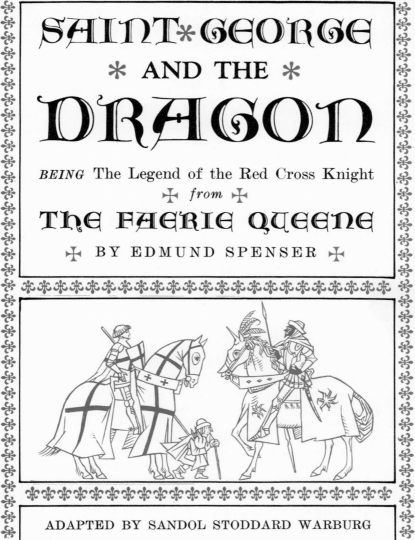

ADAPTED BY SANDOL STODDARD WARBURG

✠ *Illustrations by Pauline Baynes* ✠

HOUGHTON MIFFLIN COMPANY BOSTON

For
My Own
True and Gentle Knights:
Felix
Anthony
Peter
Gerald
and
Jason

ACKNOWLEDGMENT

I AM especially indebted to the scholarship of R. E. Neil Dodge, whose annotated edition (*The Complete Poetical Works of Spenser*, Boston: Houghton Mifflin Company, 1908) of *The Faerie Queene* has been my primary source. I would also like to express my profound gratitude and devotion to those right noble and valorous souls who have been my teachers — at Bryn Mawr College, at San Francisco State College, at Dominican College, San Rafael, California — and wherever I have found them.

S. S. W.

AUTHOR'S NOTE

THE LEGEND of Saint George and the Dragon belongs to all of us. It is the old, old story of the brave knight, the fair maiden, the castle, and the terrible fire-breathing dragon who lurks beyond the castle walls. The people of the world have dreamed this dream in many guises; for hundreds of years they have painted pictures, carved statues, written poems, sung songs, and told long winter tales about it. In our own culture, however, the story holds a place of special importance.

For in the history of a legend, as in the history of any idea, there sometimes comes a great and magical moment when commonly held material finds its perfect spokesman, its perfect place and time, its perfect form. In the case of Saint George and the Dragon, the time was the sixteenth century, the place was England, and the poet was Edmund Spenser.

The Faerie Queene came into being partly because Spenser himself lived in the days of chivalry, in a time of magnificent quests and voyages and queens and castles, when Elizabeth of England, like Gloriana in the story, sent her knights adventuring in the far corners of the earth. Spenser himself went abroad in the service of the Queen. His friend Sir Walter Raleigh founded one of the first English colonies in America — a colony which later disappeared mysteriously into the wilderness. Sir Francis Drake and other explorers sailed during these years into unknown worlds, bringing back wondrous tales of the Spice Islands, of the Bermudas, of gold and jewels and silks and treasures, and of incredible monsters that lurked in the southern seas. As you can imagine, it was a time when dragons seemed very real indeed. And the green meadows of England still held their mysteries; *Faerie Land* was an English countryside.

The right setting alone cannot, however, produce a work of art. Spenser was a very great poet — perhaps the greatest who ever lived. He had a largeness of soul, a health of mind, a compassion, an understanding, a power of invention and an absolute command of his craft which may perhaps have been equaled by one or two other poets such as Shakespeare, but which surely have never been surpassed.

Throughout the years, our best poets have loved Spenser and have honored him, often above all other teachers. Milton, Pope, Keats, and many, many others have turned to Spenser for nourishment and for instruction, as well as for the sheer joy of living for a time in the world which he created. Literary scholars and historians have made endless studies of Spenser's work; and indeed, there are so many kinds of truth in *The Faerie Queene* — historical, political, religious, philosophical, psychological — such layers upon layers of human wisdom and value — that it would take anyone a lifetime to mine its depths.

But it is not easy for us to read Spenser now, because we are not accustomed to his poetic language. He uses strange and beautiful old words which he likes to arrange in complicated, formal patterns of sound and meaning. Once we begin to understand this process, we find it as right and natural as it is for a colony of bees to construct a sturdy and graceful honeycomb, or for a growing tree to surround itself with foliage, setting out each twig and tendril in perfect balance. Spenser is telling us, in his poetry, about a vision of life in which everything has its place in the grand scheme of things. All beings strive for perfection: so man strives to be noble and good. This is what the Red Cross Knight is learning to do throughout *Saint George and the Dragon;* but Spenser believes in action even more than he believes in words, and so he offers us his lesson in the form of a tremendously exciting adventure story.

This book tells the *story* of Saint George and the Dragon just as Spenser told it. It is a translation, only very slightly shortened and simplified, of Spenser's *Faerie Queene:* Book One. In making such a translation, I have hoped to share this magnificent old legend with many new readers of all ages. But I too have had a hidden purpose, a concealed lesson in mind. My lesson has to do with poetry.

For poetry itself cannot be translated. It has worlds and worlds of special meanings in its sounds and its silences, in its shapes and arrangements and rhythms. Only the poet can tell us all he knows; we must learn how to hear it. Therefore I have tried in this book to move very gradually from the sounds and rhythmic patterns which are already familiar to us all toward those special and much more beautiful constructions which are Spenser's own.

Our modern speech is light and quick and uneven; it allows an enchanting story to unfold with great variety and speed. But it cannot really show us the world of enchantment in which Spenser's story happened. We chatter along like hurrying creeks and streams; but Spenser is like a vast and mighty ocean, where there are great swells and pools and eddies, and drifting currents, and sudden storms, and shallows and deeps, and mysteries, and moving tides, and shores of thundering surf.

So as you can see, this book is really only a way of urging you to begin reading Spenser's *Faerie Queene* as soon as possible. And when you have turned these pages, you will find (perhaps to your surprise) that you have already begun.

S. S. W.

Helpe then, O holy virgin, chiefe of nyne,
Thy weaker novice to performe thy will;
Lay forth out of thine everlasting scryne
The antique rolles, which there lye hidden still,
Of Faerie knights, and fayrest Tanaquill
Whom that most noble Briton Prince so long
Sought through the world, and suffered so much ill,
That I must rue his undeserved wrong:
O helpe thou my weake wit, and sharpen my dull tong.

From: Proem, Book 1

ℰ C A N T O ℰ I

The Red Cross Knight of Holiness
Slays Error in her den;
But soon an old man in disguise
Brings danger back again.

A noble knight was riding swiftly on the plain
Clad in mighty armor and bearing a silver shield
That was deeply dented, marked with the cruel blows
Of many a bloody battle; the arms were old, and yet
This warrior had never been to war.
His fierce horse champed against curb and bit.
The knight rode easily, like one fit
For gay jousts and tournaments,
Yet his face was solemn, almost sad.
Faithful and true he was in word and deed,
Fearless, serious and grave;
For this was the Red Cross Knight,
And on a great adventure he was bound,
Sent by the Faerie Queene,
Gloriana, mighty and magnificent
Monarch of Faerie Land. To try his untried might
A dreadful enemy awaited him: a dragon
Dangerous and frightful to behold.

And lovely beside him rode a fair lady
Upon a lowly ass more white than snow.
Yet she was whiter still
And she hid her shining face under a veil
And under a black mantle as if she held
A secret sorrow in her heart.
Heavy on her steed she sat in sadness,
Leading beside her a milk-white lamb.
As pure and innocent as that same lamb
Was the lady Una: she was the gentle daughter
And granddaughter of ancient kings and queens.
Long ago her house had ruled the world
From the Eastern to the Western shore;
But now the dreadful dragon had come to waste her lands
And drive the frightened people away;
Thus, from afar, the Red Cross Knight was summoned
To serve the Maid
And to slay the Foul Fiend.

Behind the lady lagged a little man,
A dwarf, who followed slowly on the way,
Looking lazy, or weary, perhaps,

From carrying her bag of needments at his back.
The sky was gray with clouds, and as they passed,
Rain began to pour suddenly from heaven
To the earth so furious and fast
That every living creature
Hastened to hide from the storm.
The travelers found a forest quite close by
Where trees grew so thick and broad and high

That no drop of rain
And no light of sun or of star
Could reach into that dark and secret place.
There birds were singing; there grew all the great
And lovely trees of that land:
Sapling pine,
Cedar proud and tall,
Poplar and elm
And the king of forests, builder-oak;
Cypress, aspen, laurel for conquerors and poets,
Gentle weeping willow for lovers, birch
For arrows, and myrrh

To comfort bitter pain;
Maple and beech
And ash for all good uses
And the fruitful olive tree.

Led by their delight,
The travelers wandered to and fro,
Waiting for the storm to be past;
But finally they saw that they were lost.
So many turnings, so many ways to go,
And every way unknown! They wondered how
To save themselves, or what was best to do.
At last they took a way that seemed well-used,
Trusting that it would help them to escape,
And found instead that it had brought them to
The thickest, deepest part of all the wood.
There they saw a dark and hollow cave.

The Red Cross Knight dismounted,
And Una said to him:
"Sir Knight, be cautious, be wise!

Danger here is hidden, the place unknown and wild."
"Ah lady," he replied, "it is shameful
To turn away from danger. Courage lets us see
By the light of the good that we do.
Goodness is a thing that shines: so I will find
My way in the darkness of this cave."
But Una said, "I know the danger here
Better than you, though it is now too late
To flee without dishonor and disgrace
For we have come into the Wandering Wood
And this is Error's Cave,
Where a fearful monster lives.
Therefore, Knight, be cautious,
Therefore, beware!"
"Let us go, let us go!" cried the frightened dwarf,
"This is no place for living men to be!"

But the young knight longed to try his power,
So boldly he went forth, and unafraid,
Into the cave. His glistening armor made
A shining in the dark,
And by that glooming light
He could see the ugly monster in her lair.
Partly she was like a poisonous snake
And partly like an ancient woman
Lying hideous upon the dirty ground.
Her long and loathsome tail spread all about the cave
Wound into knots
And pointed with vile stinging darts.
A thousand young ones that she daily fed
Jumped into their monster-mother's mouth

5

Hiding from the strange, shining light
Of the knight's armor, and the monster Error
Wanted to hide; but she had to fight,
For the Red Cross Knight met her, bold as a lion,
And stopped her with his sharp-cutting sword.
He struck her a mighty blow
That glanced from head to shoulder,
Wounding her sorely. Now the dreadful creature
Was truly in a rage. She leapt upon the shield
And wound around him with her crushing coils
So fierce and quick that the knight
Could move neither hand nor foot.

Now, now, Sir Knight, show what you can do!"
Cried the lady Una when she saw his plight.
"Remember your faith! Do not give way!
But strangle the monster, or she will strangle you!"
So with all his might the warrior
Tore one hand free and grasped the monster's neck
So tightly that her breath began to fail.
Then out of her throat
Came poison horrible and black
And all her stinging young
Came swarming out of hiding.
As a gentle shepherd in the sweet evening
Fumbles away a murmuring swarm
Of insects, so the knight was troubled,
But he brushed the little ones aside.
He feared the poison, yet he was more afraid
Of failure than of any danger;
With one tremendous blow he struck the head
From the body of the monster; the black blood

Flowed from her corpse, and she was dead,
And her little ones died beside her
From the poison in that foul and evil place.

Fair Knight," said Una,
"Born under a happy star,
This was your first adventure,
And your might has been great.
May all your trials bring you such glory;
May all your enemies suffer such defeat!"

Then the knight and lady looked once more
For a way out of the wood; the well-used path
Led them at last to the open air
And onward to new adventure.

Soon they chanced to meet upon the way
An aged man all clad in long, black robes.
His feet were bare, his beard was frosty gray,
And by his belt he carried a prayer book.

He seemed to be a pilgrim,
Sad, simple and wise.
(No one would have guessed, from the look
Of the man, that he was in disguise.)

The knight bowed low to him
And courteously asked him for some news
Of adventures to be found far away.
"Ah, my dear son," he replied,
"How could I know such things?
I live alone and say my prayers all day!
Yet there is one who is a foul disgrace
To knighthood — he comes often here to waste
Our lands. O Knight, if you would punish him,
Search for him in the distant wilderness."
The knight would have gone at once;
But Una said, "Ah, wait! Now comes the night
That bids us rest. Even the sun must sleep;
And you, dear sir, will find new strength this way.
You are weary from your glorious fight.
Wait, and begin new work on a new day."

And so the travelers went to the old man's house
That night with him to stay.
It was a little low place down in a dale
By a forest's side, hid in a wilderness.
Clear water played in a crystal stream
And a sacred fountain welled nearby. They came
There quietly and filled the little house,
Nor looked for entertainment where none was;
Rest was their feast and all their happiness:
For noblest minds know best content and peace.

And all the pleasant evening the old man
Told them many a sweet and curious tale
Of saints and miracles
Until their slumbering eyelids closed at last
And they slept. Then the old man went
To his study where he kept
Magic books and charms
To trouble sleepy minds;
For he was an evil man:
Archimago was his name,
And he was a great magician
Who only seemed to be a pilgrim.
Now he called up his legions of black sprites,
His guileful spirits that could float like flies
Or wing their way swiftly above the earth;
And two of these were chosen for a plot
Against the lady Una and her knight.

One small sprite flew to the twilight land
Of Morpheus, where the god of sleep lay keeping
The dreams of all the world; in a drowsy swoon

Beyond all cares, he dwelled forever sleeping
With a lulling sound of wind and moving water
Like the murmuring of bees to charm his slumber.
The lazy god awakened for a time
And, mumbling softly, lent an evil dream
To the messenger; and then he slept once more
While the little sprite flew back, light as a lark.

And as he flew, with charms and hidden arts,
Archimago made the second sprite
Into a copy of the lady Una,
Framing her tender limbs in liquid air,
Hiding her shining face under a veil
And under a black mantle as if she held
A secret sorrow in her heart.

Now the first small sprite
Hid by the heavy head of the Red Cross Knight,
Showing him false and fretful dreams of love,
Whispering lies of love to him until
He waked in a sweet confusion and beheld

The second sprite blushing beside him, tender
And lovely as his own lady,
But shedding bitter tears.

Love of yourself," she told him, "and my grief
Have stolen sleep away.
I waste the weary night in secret shame,
For I have lied to you; I have been false.

I told you of the dragon and the quest,
But truly what I wished
Was only for you to ride with me and come
To love me for your own."

The knight was deeply sad; it grieved his heart
That such a lady could be so untrue.
He comforted her gently
Before she went away
To her chamber, but in the night long after,
He lay awake in sorrow and wonder.
He did not know that sprites had tricked his eyes
And his ears; and when he slept again,
He did not know who brought him back the same
False and troubling dream.

✌ C A N T O ✌ II

The guileful great enchanter parts
Una from her knight;
Now false Duessa rides with him,
And Wrong attacks the Right.

The hour was late and many a star had set
Below the steadfast star
Northward, that guides the weary traveler
Over the wilderness and ocean waste;
And once already cheerful Chanticleer
The cock had loudly crowed to greet the dawn,
While Archimago worked with furious haste
To part the lady and her champion.

Turning the first sprite into a fair young man,
And placing him in the arms of the one
Who looked like Una, the magician ran
To wake the Red Cross Knight, calling, "Rise!
Rise, unhappy swain!
See how your faithless lady loves another!"
In all amazement then
The knight arose and followed the old man,
And saw the two sprites embrace each other

Secretly in love. The knight's anger
Flamed like fire;
He would have slain the lovers then and there,
But the great magician was too clever
To lose his sprites; he turned the knight away
And left him grieving.

He grieved, for his trust in Una now was lost;
His faithful love at last was turned to hate.
Taking the dwarf with him, he rode away
From that place in bitterness and spite
At the first dawning of the light.

When the rosy-fingered morning
Had risen fair upon the land,
The true and loyal Una
Wakened in her plain little chamber.
She looked for her knight

And her dwarf, and when she found them gone,
She began to weep;
She knew nothing of the sprites,
Of the charms or the dreams,
She knew only that her knight
Had fled; and she rode
After him as swiftly as her slow
Beast could go.

But the Red Cross Knight spurred his light-foot steed
Onward in anger and disdain.
Una searched hill and wood and dale
All in vain. To follow him was useless weariness,
Yet she could not rest,
For she was sorely hurt in her gentle heart
That he whom she loved best
Had so ungently left her.
Wicked Archimago rejoiced.
Whatever was noble, true and good
He wished to destroy. He would
Follow the lady, he decided,
And do her whatever harm he could.

Now the magician planned a new disguise;
He knew such mighty spells that he could take
As many forms and shapes
As the sea-god Proteus.
Sometimes he would make
Himself into a fox, or a snake,
Or a fish in a lake,

And sometimes he would be
A dragon so horrible that he
Would frighten himself, and shake,
And quake, and have to run away!

But now he seemed to be the Red Cross Knight,
Dressed in mighty armor and bearing a silver shield;
So easily he rode,
So fearless, serious and grave did he appear,

That no one would have guessed
What an evil man hid
In that armor, what a coward wore
The great sign of the Cross upon his breast.

But Una's knight had wandered far away
Still flying from his thoughts and jealous fear.

Will was his guide, and grief led him astray.
At last he chanced to meet upon the way
A Saracen, a huge man armed to fight,
Carrying a shield that read "SANS FOI."
A reckless knight he was, who cared not a pin
For God or man,
And with him rode a fair companion,
A gay lady dressed in scarlet red,
Jingling with jewelry and trinkets of all kinds,
And little golden bells
On her horse's bridle
Ringing as she rode.

Sans Foi was full of wrath and pride,
And when he saw the Knight of the Red Cross,
Quickly he spurred his mighty horse
To battle. The red blood
Ran down the sides
Of the beast, and the warriors met with a shock
That staggered both. Backward they reeled

And paused in astonishment;
As when two rams
Stirred with ambitious pride
Fight for the rule of the rich fleeced flock,
So these two stood together locked,
Their broken weapons hanging idly by.
The Saracen, who had been sorely hurt,
Was first to reach his sword. In a rage he dashed
At the Red Cross Knight, who gave back blow for blow;
And so fiercely did they fight
That sparks, like the fire from a forge,
Flew from their shields and swords where they clashed,
And streams of purple blood flowed
Over the blooming fields.

Curse upon that Cross," cried the Saracen,
"It keeps your body safe from bitter death!
I would have killed you long ago had not
That charm protected you! But now, stand fast,
I warn you, hide your head!"
And he tried to strike, but the Red Cross Knight
Cut with all his might
At the helmet of the Saracen;
The steel was split;
The head was crushed beneath,
And proud Sans Foi came tumbling down alive
With bloody mouth to kiss his mother earth
And greet his grave; his ghost soon flew away
To the place where evil souls go after death.

The lady, when she saw her champion fall
Like the old ruins of a broken tower,

Shed no tears for him, but turned and fled
As fast as she could go. The Red Cross Knight
Called to the dwarf to carry off the shield
Of Sans Foi as a sign of victory
And hastened after the lady
Telling her to have no fear.
She cried, "O mercy, mercy on me, sir!
My sad misfortunes put me in your power,
And I am subject to your mighty will!"
Such humble speech from one so richly dressed
Made the valiant heart of the Red Cross Knight
Soften and grow tender toward her.
"Dear lady," he replied, "I do regret
Your sudden sorrow, but put fear aside;
Tell me your name — and who was your champion?"

Melting into tears,
The lady began to lament.
She told him of her life
A long and sorrowful tale;
She swore to him she was
An emperor's only child;
Fidessa was her name,

20

She said, and the Saracen,
That wicked man, had forced
Her to ride with him.

There were, she explained, three brothers,
Born of one bad sire:
The eldest was proud Sans Foi,
The youngest was Sans Joi,
And in between was bloody bold
Sans Loi. "Ah me," she wept,
"In helpless misery
I wander the lonely world —
If you do me no good, dear sir,
O do me no harm!"

Fair lady," replied the Red Cross Knight, who gazed
At her dainty face and did not listen well,
"A heart of flint would mourn your sorry plight.
But now you have lost a foe and found a friend!
Ride on with me; let grief be at an end!"

And so they rode together, until the golden sun
Had mounted high, and Phoebus hurled his beams
Down scorching hot; then, weary of the way,
The travelers came to a place where two fair trees
Spread wide their arms with green and trembling leaves
Shading the winds and shadowing the earth.
The country shepherds feared the solemn place,
Saying that it was haunted and unlucky,
But the knight and his new lady
Hastened there to rest in the cooling breeze.
And as she kept him pleasant company,

21

Smiling shyly,
Speaking to him sweetly,
In his false fancy
The knight believed her fair.
He believed her a princess, and wishing to crown
Her lovely head with leaves, he plucked down
A little branch from the tree above his head.

Out of the tree came trickling drops of blood
And a piteous moaning voice on high was heard
Crying "Spare me, spare me, do not tear
My tender sides though they are hidden here
Within the bark of a tree — but fly away!
Fly far away for fear that the evil day
May come to you, O Knight, that came to me,
And to my lady in the neighbor tree!"

The good knight's hair stood out upon his head,
He was so horror-struck. But finally
He found his voice and cried,
"What voice of ghost condemned or guileful sprite
Calls me from empty air?"

22

No ghost," answered the tree, "no guileful sprite,
But once a Man of Doubt, Fradubio,
Now to a tree transformed by craft and spite.
Here must I stand while icy winds and rains
And blazing suns destroy my hidden flesh,
For though I am a tree, I feel these pains."

Say on, Fradubio, whether man or tree,"
The knight replied. "There is good medicine
In telling how our troubles came to be;
The heart is heavy that must hide its grief."

A wicked witch has caused my wretchedness,"
Answered the tree, "and many a foolish knight
Has she betrayed by making them doubt Truth.
Duessa is her name,
And this is how she lured me to my fate:

In the gallant years of youth when my blood ran hot
And the fire of love and the joy of chivalry
First kindled in my breast, it was my lot
To serve this gentle lady whom you see
Beside me hidden in the neighbor tree.
Riding together once we met a knight
And with him rode a fair companion,
A gay lady dressed in scarlet red,
Jingling with jewelry and trinkets of all kinds,
And little golden bells
On her horse's bridle
Ringing as she rode.

The unknown champion challenged me to fight
In the name of his dainty lady and her beauty;
My own was fairer far, and I gladly fought,
And as it chanced, he fell beneath my spear:
Such is the luck of war.
Now I had two ladies to defend;
But Duessa wished to be
The only one, and cruelly she cast
A magic spell, a dark and foggy mist
Over the beauty of my former love
That made me leave her. So did I doubt my love
That I rode in joy with that gay and scarlet witch,
And then she stole my lady away
To this tree in the wilderness.

But each year in the spring there is one day
When every witch is punished for her crimes;
Upon that day, she may use no disguise
(And underneath a witch's beauty is
A loathsome creature who cannot wash clean
No matter how she tries).
At such a time, I found Duessa bathing
In perfumes and sweet spices by a stream
And I saw that she was a monster all misshapen,
Foul as her evil soul. I fled from her,
But she caught me, and she carried me away
Drowned in a magic sleep to this far country
Beside my lady to become a tree."
"How long then enchanted must you stay
Within these wooden walls?" inquired the knight.
"Only the water from a living well,"
Replied Fradubio, "can unbind the spell."

The Red Cross Knight, lamenting for his sake,
Turned to his own companion
And found that she had fainted dead away.
Terror had made her swoon,
For she herself was that gay and scarlet one
Who had betrayed Fradubio, and she knew
Only too well that his sad tale was true.
But the knight was far too innocent and good
To guess a thing so terrible. He held
Her close to comfort her and soothed her fears,
And when she waked, he helped her mount her steed.
So to the trees a sad farewell they said,
And forward slowly rode.

⚓ C A N T O ⚓ III

Forsaken Una seeks her knight
And makes the lion mild;
Halts a heartless thief and meets
A warrior fierce and wild.

Nothing under the wide hollow of heaven
Awakens deeper pity and regret
Than beauty suffering
Of such a one I sing:
Una, daughter of a king,
True as touchstone,
Fair as ever living soul was fair,
Faithful in word and deed,
Deserving no evil,
But from her knight parted in despair;
Forsaken, woeful, solitary maid,
Far from human kind
In wilderness and desert wastes wandering
Alone, yet unafraid.

One day, weary of her journey,
She stepped from her slow-moving steed
And laid her gentle limbs down on the grass

In secret shadow far from all men's sight.
From her fair head she put aside the veil
And the black mantle, so that her angel's face
Shone as bright as the great eye of heaven,
Making a sunshine in the shady place;
Never did mortal eyes behold such grace.

Then it chanced that out of the thick, deep wood
Came suddenly a wild and roaring lion
Hungry for flesh and blood;
And when he saw the innocent royal maid,
With gaping mouth he ran at her greedily
Meaning to devour her tender body.

27

But as he drew close, his bloody rage grew less;
Seeing her shining face,
He knew at once within his savage heart
That it would be wrong to hurt her.
Instead, he sank down kissing her weary feet,
Licking her pure white hands in sympathy:
So can Beauty master the most strong,
And simple Truth can triumph over Wrong.

Una was waiting still in dread of death
But when she saw that the lion meant to be
Her friend, at last she wept
In joy and solemn pity.
"The lion, lord of every beast in the field,"
She said, "is kind and humble at my feet.
But he, my lion, my own noble knight,
How does he find it in his cruel heart
To hate me? Why has he left me thus?" Her cries
Were softly echoed from the neighboring wood,
And sorrowful, the kingly beast stood by
Gazing gently on her tears. At last she rose,
Within her quiet heart closing her pain,
And rode to seek her champion again.

The lion would not leave her all alone,
But went along with her, as a strong guard
And a faithful friend to all her grief and woe.
When Una slept, he lay awake and watched,
And when she waked, he waited by her side
To do her humble service.
Looking into her eyes, he understood
Her wishes and obeyed her least command.
Long they traveled now through wide

Wastelands and wilderness
Until they came to a place where the long grass
Was trodden down with footprints, and they spied
A young girl walking under the mountainside
Bearing a pot of water upon her shoulders.
When they drew nearer, Una called to her,
Asking if there were any house close by
Where they might rest, but the girl was proud and rude,
And she would not answer. Then she saw the lion,
And she threw her pitcher down and ran away,
Never looking behind.

home she went, where her old mother blind
In darkness huddled all day mumbling rhymes
And secret charms that pleased her foolish mind.
The women shook with fear when Una came
Gently to the door, begging for shelter;

They had no human kindness to offer
Nor friendship for the maiden who brought
Light to their dark corner,
But the lion cleared the way and Una entered,
Telling the women not to be afraid.

The day was spent and now came drowsy night
When every creature sinks to rest and sleep;
Now sadly Una lay for weariness
Down in the dark; and faithful at her feet
The lion kept his watch while Una wept
Mourning the loss of her dear champion.
The night was long, for it was full of tears;
She could not rest, but waited for the light.

Now when late-shining stars looked down upon the world,
And all below lay drowned in deadly sleep,

There came a sudden knocking at the door;
A man was there, with a heavy load at his back.
And he began to curse and shout and swear
When no one let him into the house at once.
He was a heartless thief who robbed the poor
And stripped the churches of their ornaments
While good men slept; then in the night he crept
With his loot to visit the old woman's daughter,
Who was his secret love. He gave her gold
And stolen jewelry, and he fed her fat
With plundered foods and feasts;
But tonight she did not dare to open the door,
For fear of the lion. Furiously and more
Furiously he pounded; then he would wait
No longer; shouting with rage, he broke down the door,
And entered, wild with anger.
With one great paw the lion struck him down.
He cursed no more, nor dared to make a sound.
The thirsty earth drank up his ebbing blood,
And his torn corpse lay upon the ground.

At last the world awoke to shining day;
Up rose Una, and up the lion rose
Once more to wander on their weary way,
But the women of the house began to howl
And shriek, seeing their useful swain lie dead.
They followed Una, cursing her bitterly,
Until she was out of sight.
Then turning away, they spied a knight nearby
Clad in mighty armor and bearing a silver shield:
It was the great magician in disguise,
Seeking Una to do what harm he could.

The angry women were quick to point the way,
And soon he followed quietly and close,
Waiting for her to see the great Red Cross.

And so she did; in tears she came to him,
Saying, "Ah, my long-lacked lord,
Where have you been so long out of my sight?
Why have you thus forsaken me?
So have I feared your hate,
So have I trembled since you went away,
My cheerful day has turned to cheerless night;
Welcome, dear light and shining lamp of bliss!"

And Archimago cleverly replied:
"Ah, dearest lady, sooner shall the earth
Forget to bring forth fruits than I forget
My much-beloved maid of royal birth,
The one I serve with all my heart; and yet
Archimago showed me a great quest,
And lady, many a true and faithful knight
Have I delivered from captivity
Since duty called me from your gracious sight.
Now I return, and now by land and sea,
I swear I shall defend you faithfully."

Una believed his words: one loving hour
Can pay for years of anger and disdain;
An ounce of sweet is worth a pound of sour,
And true love never gazes back on pain.

Now as the ocean wanderer comes back
Cheerful and whistling to the busy port,
So gay was Una, and as the merchant glad
To see his ship come home
Blesses the winds and thanks the lucky seas,
So she went forth in joy and merriment,
Telling the knight of every happening
Since they had parted and of the faithful beast
Who went beside her still. Then suddenly
They saw a knight come toward them galloping
On a fierce and mighty steed;
The rider's face was bold and threatening;

Upon his shield they read the words "SANS LOI."
And as soon as the rider spied the great sign
Of the Red Cross, he set his spear to charge;
For such a knight had slain his elder brother,
And his anger blazed like fire.
Archimago shook with fear;
So proud and furious came the Saracen
So full of wrath, that his sharp-headed spear
Pierced the magician's shield with a single blow.
The old man fell; his blood began to flow;
Dismounting swiftly then,
Sans Loi cried, "Such is the well-deserved end
Of the one who slew Sans Foi! My brother's ghost
May now pass over Lethe Lake in peace;
He is revenged!" And swiftly he unlaced
The helmet of his fallen foe to deal
The final blow, but Una cried, "O hold,
Hold, sir, for mercy's sake!
When fortune smiled on him, this champion
Fought well in the field. Now you have won the day,
But do not take his life from him, I pray,
For he is the truest knight under the sun!"

Sans Loi cared nothing for her piteous words;
Roughly he tore the helmet off
And would have killed the old man on the spot,
But when he spied that frosty-bearded head,
He stood amazed and wondered at the sight,
Saying, "Why Archimago, luckless sir,
I would not injure you!
Why does the great magician fight his true
And faithful friend in such a strange disguise?"

35

But Archimago answered not a word;
He fell in a swoon, and on those guileful eyes
Lay the dark cloud of death. Una was mocked
By the magician's trick; gone was her joy;
She stood and watched in silent misery.
Then roughly Sans Loi plucked her from her steed
And seized her veil to tear it from her face.
But the lion, seeing his dear gentle lady
So rudely handled, charged with gaping jaws
And would have torn the warrior's shield away.
Alas, Sans Loi drew forth his deadly sword
And then the power of the simple beast
Was all too weak. The lordly heart was pierced,
The plunging iron thrust his breath away,
He roared aloud, and life forsook his breast.

Now who will keep the forlorn maid from harm?
Her faithful guardian gone,
She is at the mercy of Sans Loi.

On his swift horse he carries her away
In spite of all her piteous laments.
Her gentle steed, who would not leave her so,
Follows to share her woe:
A beast far milder than the beastly foe.

❧ C A N T O ❧ I V

To the sinful House of Pride
Duessa brings the knight;
There Sans Joi, seeking revenge,
Challenges him to fight.

Young knight at arms, whoever you may be,
If you would do good works and virtuous deeds,
Beware of foolishness in love. Beware
Of easily believing that your friend is to blame
Or of changing too lightly your choice;
For to a knight there is no greater shame
Than faithlessness. This we may plainly see
Proved by the example of the Red Cross Knight:
He left his lady, who was ever true,
And rode with a witch, believing all her lies.

And long they traveled, till at last they saw
A glittering building, gay with ornaments,
That seemed to be the palace of a prince.
This was the House of Pride:
And toward it ran a great highway worn bare
By the traffic of many feet;
Great troops of people traveled there

Both day and night, but few came back again,
For in that place they met with foul disgrace
And afterward they lay alone and sick
In roadside ditches, begging for their bread.
Duessa told the knight to ride that way,
For she was weary at the close of day.

The stately palace rose before their eyes:
Its walls were high, but neither strong nor thick,
Since, without mortar, they were made of brick,
And covered with golden foil
That shamed the shining sky with brilliancy.
High lifted up was many a lofty tower
With many a gate and pleasant gallery
Full of fair windows and delightful bowers;
It was a pity that so fair a house
Should stand so weak upon a sandy hill:
Each breath of wind from heaven shook it all
From top to bottom, and the sand slid down
Continually. Behind, its hidden parts
Were old and ruined, but painted cleverly.
The travelers entered into the great hall
Which was ablaze with splendid tapestries
And rich display; the Prince of Persia's court
Never beheld so sumptuous a show
Of wealth; and there a proud and princely crew
Of lords and ladies stood on every side
Adding their beauty to the brilliant scene.

High above all a cloth of state was spread
And a rich throne, as bright as sunny day,
Where sat a queen, in gorgeous array,

A maiden queen shining like the sun
In glittering gold and peerless precious stones;
And she exceeding shone
Like Phoebus' fairest child who kindled heaven,
Proud, foolish, wild,
Wrapped in whirling wheels
Of fire not made to burn, but meant to shine.

So great her shining was that she disdained
The lowly earth. Beneath her scornful feet
A dreadful dragon lay with hideous train
And in her hand she held a mirror bright
Wherein she gazed with love and swollen pride.
Lucifera was her name;
She was haughty, evil, vain,
And not a rightful queen,
But one who ruled her stolen lands by plot
And trickery, with wizards at her side.

As soon as the Red Cross Knight and false Duessa
Came into the presence of the throne,
They knelt most humbly, telling the proud queen
That they had come to view her majesty
And praise her royal state;
But she would hardly let her eyes look low
Enough to see them, or to bid them rise.
Meantime all her lords and ladies preened
And prinked their curls to meet the travelers' sight,
Greeting Duessa fondly, and welcoming the knight.

Suddenly the royal lady rose,
Calling for her coach, and the people rode
Each other's shoulders watching her go by.
Bright as the dawn and clothed in glittering light
Abroad she came, and climbed into her coach
That was adorned with flowers and with gold
Like Juno's royal chariot. But peacocks
Did not pull Lucifera's shining coach:
Hers was drawn by six unequal beasts
With six magicians riding on their backs,
Who were the queen's chief counselors at court.

The first was sluggish *Idleness,*
Who slowly led the way
Riding upon a lazy ass,
So drowned in sleep he could not guess
If it were night or day.

And by his side rode *Gluttony*
Upon a filthy swine;
He was so foul and fat that he
Could barely move or think or see,
From gobbling food and wine.

And next to him *Dishonesty*
Upon a bearded goat:
A man who loved to cheat and lie,
He hid his ugly cruelty
Under a fair green coat.

Riding a camel, *Avarice* told
His coins in bulging bags:
He had sold his soul for gold,
Yet he himself was sick and old,
Starving, and in rags.

And *Envy* followed close beside,
Riding a wolf: he kept
His eye upon his neighbor's pride,
And wishing it were his, he sighed,
And gnashed his teeth, and wept.

Then *Anger* with his bloody knife
On a raging lion last:
He spent his strength on hate and strife
And fretting grief, the foe of life,
When the wild fit was past.

And after all, upon the wagon beam
Rode Satan, with a cruel whip in hand
With which he often lashed the lazy team.
Huge crowds of people stood along the way
Shouting for Lucifera and for joy;
A foggy mist had covered all the land
And underneath their feet all scattered lay
Dead bones of men whose lives had gone astray.
So forth they marched into the open air
Over the fields that seemed to them so fine
And foul Duessa, that false lady fair
Rode by the glittering queen,
But the Red Cross Knight refused to come so near;
He did not care to share such fellowship.
Thus having entertained themselves a space,
Back they turned to the palace once again
And there they found an angry knight at arms
Newly arrived and seeking fierce revenge.
His heart was full of fury, wrath, and hate:
His shield in letters red proclaimed "SANS JOI."

And when he saw his brother's shield, he leapt
Upon the dwarf who carried it,
But swiftly the Red Cross Knight
Went to the rescue, for the prize was his
And fairly won.
With that, they went to battle, shield and sword,
Until their noise and clamor
Troubled all the company,
And the great glittering queen
Upon eternal pain
Of high displeasure told them to refrain.

If either one, she said, had any right
To own the shield, tomorrow then they might
Resolve their quarrel in fair and equal fight.

"Ah dearest lady," said the bold Sans Joi,
"Pardon the error of a man in grief.
I could not bear to see this traitor knight
Who killed my brother in a treacherous fight,
Who reaps the harvest sown by his foe,
Sown in the bloody field and bought with woe."

The Red Cross Knight said little; for he meant
With swords and not with words to plead his right.
He cast his gauntlet as a sacred pledge
To try his cause in combat the next day
And so they parted, with their hearts on edge,
Each for revenge against his enemy.

The evening passed in joy and jollity,
With feasting in bower and hall
Until dark night had spread
Her curtains over all
And sleep had stilled the courtly company.

Then up rose Duessa from her resting place,
And came on silent feet to seek Sans Joi,
Who lay awake in gloomy, fretful mind.
"Ah, dear Sans Joi," she said, "next to Sans Foi
Most dear: lo, his Fidessa flies to you!"
With gentle words he greeted her
And bade her tell the secret of her heart.
Then sighing soft she said, "I learn, oh oft
A little sweetness brings a deal of pain!
For since I loved and lost my dear Sans Foi
I never had an hour
Of joy. That wicked man,
The Red Cross Knight, who unworthy won his shield,
Dragged me away — me, a helpless maid,
And now he keeps me down in a dark cave,
Because I will not love him. Ah, but you
Come to my life like sunlight after storms!
The love I gave your brother now is yours.
Let not his love, let not his restless ghost
Go unrevenged! O save his shield, and me!"

To that he answered, "Do not weep, fair maid,
For sorrows that are past, nor be afraid
Of present danger. Grief or fear's a waste."

Oh, but I dread the fortunes of the field,"
She answered, "and he bears a magic shield
And arms enchanted that no man can pierce;
No one can wound him!" Sans Joi answered fierce,
"Charmed or enchanted makes no difference.
I pay no mind to that; neither should you.
But fair Fidessa, since of fate or foe
You are prisoner, go and rest a while.
Tomorrow I will win you and the shield;
Tomorrow the Red Cross Knight shall die."
"Ay me," she sighed, "it is a double death
While I am grieving now, to see his pride.
Yet I will go, and send you secret aid
Wherever I may be." So she obeyed.

❧ C A N T O ❧ V

The faithful knight upon the field
Defeats his faithless foe;
Duessa saves Sans Joi, and for
his cure to hell they go.

The noble heart, that harbors virtuous thought,
Can never rest till glorious deeds are done;
So restless passion kept the Red Cross Knight
Wakeful and watching till the dawning light.
At last he saw great heaven's golden gate
Begin to open; Phoebus fresh and fair
Came dancing forth, shaking his dewy hair
And hurled his glittering beams down the dim air.

Up rose our knight, and to his sun-bright arms;
Forth he came; into the common hall
Where early awaited many a gazing eye,
Where many a minstrel made sweet melody
With stories of old loves and ancient wars.
Soon came the stern Sans Joi in woven mail;
With cruel eyes he stared upon his foe,
But the Red Cross Knight cared not a pin
What man looked on him so.

Then both were given rare Arabian wines
And dainty spice from far-off India
To stir the courage of the secret heart;
And with the wine they made a solemn vow
To keep the sacred laws of tournaments.
At last came forth the famous royal queen
To sit in state beneath a canopy
Upon a square of green;
Across the way, in all men's open view,
Sat fair Duessa by the bloody shield.

A shrilling trumpet sounded from on high;
With eager force they leapt to the attack,
Whirling their burning blades above their heads,
Heaping their blows like iron hammers down.
Sans Joi was stout and strong,
The Red Cross Knight was full of heat;
Both stricken struck, and beaten both men beat
Until their shields sent forth a fiery light;
And both their cruel swords so greedy bit
The tender flesh that streams of blood flowed down.
The armor that had been so bright
Was dyed a pure vermilion;
And pity grew in all the watchers' hearts;
They dared not wish that either man would win.

At last by chance the furious Sans Joi
Glanced at the bloody prize
And cried: "Ah, wretched son of woeful sire!
Your shield hangs here in shame!
And does your hapless brother fail you now?"
With that, he struck the knight upon the crest

Until he reeled and started twice to fall.
The watchers thought the fight was won,
And false Duessa loudly began to call
"The shield is yours, Sans Joi, and I, and all!"

But when he heard the sound of his lady's voice
The Red Cross Knight rose from his swooning dream;
Rousing his failing faith,
In wrath and shame, and for his lady's sake,
He hurled the proud Sans Joi down to his knees.
"Go, wretched knight," he cried.
"Go bring this message to your brother dear!
Tell him I won your shield to hang with his!"
Swiftly he raised his heavy hand on high
To slay Sans Joi, when lo! a dark cloud fell
Over the foe. He disappeared from sight;
Our knight called him aloud. No answer came,
For he had vanished into the shrouding dark.

Running in haste, Duessa cried, "O Knight,
Bravest that ever lady chose to love,
Now let your vengeance and your fury sleep!
Lo! the infernal powers
Cover your foe and carry him away
To hell's dark house, to Pluto's baleful bowers.
I and the shield and victory are yours!"

Not satisfied, the Red Cross Knight looked round
And stood amazed, wondering how Sans Joi
Could hide in the secret shade —
And then he heard the trumpets blare and blaze.
Now running heralds paid him humble praise;

They brought the shield to him; then to the queen
He knelt in homage. The people clapped with glee;
Their shouts filled all the high and shining air.

Home he was brought and there
Laid in a great soft bed;
The wisest surgeons came to care
For all his wounds that freshly bled.
About the bed sweet melody
Was played to ease his agony
And all the while most bitterly
Duessa wept.

Until the evening lamps in Jove's high house
Were lit, she wept her false beguiling tears.
Then she arose and silently stole away
To the enchanted place where Sans Joi lay
Swooning as she had left him, in the cloud.
She did not linger there,
But to the eastern coast of heaven sped.
There grisly Night
With face so deadly sad
In pitch-black mantle clad
Came from the cave where she so darkly hid.
And when she saw Duessa sunny bright,
Adorned with gold and jewels shining clear,
She trembled at the sight
And would have turned away from her in fear,
But then the crafty witch began to speak:
"Hail, O most ancient grandmother of all,
Who saw the secrets of the world unmade,

Older than Jove, older than all the gods,
Wait while I tell my tale:

Why have you let your own dear nephews fail
In battle where the children of the light
Have triumphed? My beloved bold Sans Foi
Lies in the field while birds pick clean his bones;
Lo, how Sans Joi sleeps in the deadly shade!
What does it mean to be
Born of the gods, born of the dreaded Night,
When her own offspring are so foul forlorn?
Up then! Up, mournful dame, great midnight's queen!
Come gather up the remnants of your race,
Or else avenge them, so it may be seen
That dreaded Night can keep her honored place."

The lady replied, "Dear daughter, I do mourn
The fall of famous children born to me,
But who can turn the stream of Destiny?
Great Jove who rules Fate and Necessity
Favors the Sons of Light
And by my ruin thinks to make them great.
Yet he who killed Sans Foi shall pay for it
With his own blood. My child, what is your name?"

I am Duessa, dressed in scarlet red,
I am disguised, and yet I am the same:
Duessa, daughter of Deceit and Shame."

O welcome, child! How I have longed for you!
I am the first of all your family!
Lo, I will give you aid;
Come with me."

So to her iron chariot they climbed
And flew through the murky air.
The team was unequally paired
And yet they softly swam;
They never stamped unless their reins were plucked —
Then, foaming dark with tar,
They reared and tramped the air.
Swiftly they sped to the enchanted place
Where Sans Joi lay all smeared with mud and blood.
They bound his dreadful wounds as best they could
And laid him gently down in the coach of iron.

And all the time that Night stood on the ground
The dogs were barking in the horrid dark;
With dreary shrieks the owl,

Messenger of death, called out,
And hungry wolves kept up a gloomy howl.
Softly at last they stole

Back with the heavy body to the gulf
Of deep Avernus hole,
The gate of hell, that smoke and sulphur hid.
That way they drove the chariot
Down to the house of Pluto underground
Past all the ghosts and furies of the dark,
Past all the wicked sprites that trick men's eyes
And tease their brains with falsehood,
Past dreadful Cerberus who lay
Watching the gates with three great ugly heads
That slept by turns, with poisonous snaky curls

56

And flaming tongues;
And at last they came to a hidden cave
Hollowed with wondrous craft
In the deepest, dark, most doleful place of all.
There dwelt a wizard skilled in medicine
Who paid with continual pain
An endless penance for a life of sin.
Bearing the wounded champion in her arms,
There ancient Night stepped down.
"Give me," she begged the wizard, "herbs or charms
To call my nephew back from the door of death!"

Ah lady," he replied, "these were the arts
That thrust me out of heaven.
Should I repeat the crime of sorcery?
Can Night herself protect her subjects from
The wrath of Jove who rules both Night and Day?"
"No," she replied, "but since great heaven's king
Has taught you that there is no hope for you,
Why fear his power? He cannot hurt you more.

Come then, and show us all your famous skills!"
After a time her prayers and praises won;
His healing hands began to cast their spells.
The mother of dread darkness rose again,
Leaving her nephew in the wizard's care;
And turning back, she flew through the murky air
Her usual way, until her course was run
At the rising of the sun.

Duessa traveled to the House of Pride,
Great Lucifera's palace whence she came,
And there she found that the wounded Red Cross Knight
Had fled unhealed, unready yet to ride.
He had good cause to hasten thus away:
The wary dwarf had spied
About the palace and had found the truth.
Down in deep dungeons throngs of captives lay,
As sorry a sight as ever eyes have seen.
They were the slaves of Pride;
All having given up their lives to greed

And sloth and envy lay
Condemned to live in wrath and die in woe.
There wailed all day the King of Babylon
Who long ago made nations call him God.
There lay King Croesus, who loved only gold,
And warlike Nimrod, first to waste the world
With fire and sword; and many a queen and prince
Who had lived a life of idle pomp and play,
Wasting the hours and consuming goods,
Insulting God and man.

And when the cautious dwarf
Had told his master of their mournful plight,
The knight rose early, fearing that he might share
That well-deserved fate. Before the dawn
He fled by a secret gate;
His death was certain if they saw him go.
But he could scarcely find a way to ride
Behind the castle walls;
For there lay carcasses of murdered men
Unburied and unmourned on every side:
This was the shameful truth that lay behind
The sorry splendor of the House of Pride.

CANTO VI

Una through wondrous grace is saved
From Sans Loi by a band
Of forest folk who worship her
And hear her wise command.

As when a ship sails barely by a rock
That would have wrecked it, and the captain stares
Amazed, ashamed, and grateful for his luck;
So when our knight escaped the House of Pride,
His thoughts lay in a strange confusion
Of joy and pain
And he was sad to leave without the fair
Duessa, yet more sad
Than any loss was still his loss of faith
In Una, lady of his love and grief,
Una, his dear dread.

She in her innocence
Had wandered to the corners of the earth
Searching for him, and would have wandered still,
But she was now the prisoner of Sans Loi,
And he had led her into a deep, wild wood.

With flattering words he courted her awhile,
With tempting looks and many a guileful sigh
He sought her love; but Una's honest heart
Was steadfast as a diamond, single and pure.
At last, to feast his eyes upon her face,
He snatched her veil away;
Her beauty blazing like the brightest skies
Inflamed his greed; he took her in his arms
By force; and now she sent up piteous cries
To heaven for help in her extreme distress.
The stars began to fall like tears of fire
And Phoebus hid his sunny face in shame;
What mortal man could save the maiden now?
But God's great Providence
Supplied a wondrous way:
A band of fauns and satyrs in the wood
Were dancing merrily; far off they heard
That piteous straining voice and came in haste.
When they drew near, the raging Saracen
Was filled with fear, seeing their shapes so wild
And strange; he ran to his steed, and rode away.

The wild wood-gods stood round about the maid
And stared, and wondered at her woeful state.
Her veil was tumbled and her shining face
Was wet with tears. She wept and trembled still:
The simple creatures were amazed to see
Beauty so bright distressed so cruelly.
She, more amazed, looked back and did not dare
To speak or move; and silently they gazed
At one another till the creatures saw
Her fear; then they took off their frowning masks,

Their horns, and all their rough and rustic gear.
They felt a tender sorrow new to them,
A solemn pity and a strange regret;
Gently they grinned, and came to comfort her;
Humbly they kneeled down to kiss her feet.

Then unafraid the lady arose, and all
Around her as she walked,
Glad as young goats they leapt on horny feet

Shouting aloud and singing shepherds' rhymes
Sweet as the birds of spring;
They strewed the ground with branches gay and green.
Crowned her with leaves, and worshiped her as queen.

And they played their merry pipes along the way
Till all the woodlands answered, and their echoing
Woke old Sylvanus in his shady grove;
Leaning his ancient limbs upon a staff,

The king of forests came
To see the cause of all their joy, and stood
Astonished before Una's shining form.
The ancient god did not know what to think.
Her beauty was like nothing earthly born.
Goddess of Love he thought her, but he knew
Venus never showed such solemn grace;
Goddess of Purity, Diana bright,
She might be then — but held no hunting bow.
Who was she? All his early loves came back
To haunt him as he gazed. The fauns bowed down
Worshiping her, and the little nymphs flocked near
To stare and sigh with envy at her face,
That was the perfect form and flower of faith.

Glad of her luck, the sad unlucky maid
Was satisfied to please their innocent eyes;
And there she stayed
To rest her soul from misery a while,
Teaching the forest people to love God
And worship Him alone. But all they knew
Of worshiping, they spent on things and shapes
And shadows of the truth. They would not learn
Her holy ways; and when she would not let
Them worship her, they found her milk-white steed
And worshiped it.

Now to that forest wild
There came a noble knight
Whose glorious deeds were told
All over Faerie Land.
His name was Satyrane:

He was a satyr's son,
Born of a gentle lady
Stolen into the wood.

In the tender days of youth
He had grown to forest ways
Among the wild beasts
Far from the laws of men.
His father forced him then
To fear no creature,
Placing his trembling hand
Upon the bear and lion.

But soon his father trembled
And his loving mother wept
When she crept into the wood
To see her little boy;
For young Satyrane
Had learned a lesson wilder
Than his teacher: he was tyrant
Of every prowling creature.

The lion and the bear,
The roaring bull and boar,
The wolf and spotted panther
All were in his power.
He tamed them and mastered them,
Made them his servants,
Rode upon their backs,
And teased them for his sport.

When he was full-grown,
And gentler and wiser,

This champion had gone
Abroad to new adventure;
Now he came riding
Home to seek his father,
After long labors
And many a brave deed.

And when he saw fair Una in the wood,
Teaching the satyrs true and holy ways,
He wondered at her wisdom; finding her deeds
Good as her words, he longed to keep her faith
And be her true and loyal champion.
But Una, mourning in her secret heart
For the Red Cross Knight, longed only to escape.

Satyrane agreed to find a way,
And soon there came a day
When the forest people went to serve their king,
Leaving the maiden and the knight alone.
Then from the wood he led her swift and sure,
Onto the darkling plain.

65

Satyrs will hunt and hail her back in vain:
For if we fail to hold what once we have,
There is no way to bring it back again.

Traveling now by twilight soon they spied
A weary soul who wandered by the way,
An aged man all clad in long black robes.
His beard was frosty gray
And by his belt he carried a prayer book.
He seemed to be a pilgrim,
Sad, simple and wise;
And Satyrane came hastening near to ask
Tidings of war and news
Of adventures to be found far away.
"Ah, my dear son," he replied.
"How could I know such news?
I live alone and say my prayers all day!"
Then Una asked him of a champion
In sun-bright arms, bearing a great Red Cross.

"Ah me, dear lady, how it saddens me,"
The old man answered, "how I grieve to say
I saw that champion, first alive, then dead."

His cruel words so pierced her tender heart
That the lady fell into a deadly swoon;
But Satyrane comforted her gently,
And Una summoned strength to hear the rest,
Now that the worst was past.

Then said the pilgrim, "On the fatal day
I chanced to see two knights (a sorry sight!)
Angry and fierce, preparing for a fight;
They fought, they bled, I trembled for my life;
What more is there to say? A Saracen
Has slain the Red Cross Knight."

How can that be?" cried Una.
"The noblest knight that ever fought and won!"
"I saw it happen," answered the old man,
"How could I see a thing that was not done?"

Where is that Saracen?" cried Satyrane,
"That son of darkness who has slain our joy?"

Not far away," the sly old man replied,
"Washing his cruel wounds beside
A fountain where I left him."

And so good Satyrane
Rode on in haste while Una followed slow,
Heavy with grief and woe.

And soon he came to a place
In secret shadow by a fountainside
Where the Saracen lay resting from his fight.
He was none other than the same Sans Loi
Who had stolen Una, carrying her away
Into the wood; and as soon as Satyrane
Spied him, he cried: "Arise!
O cursed traitor! You have foully shamed
The cause of chivalry if you have slain
The Red Cross Knight! Rise and defend your wrong,
Or yield in sorrow to his champion!"
Sans Loi arose in haste and buckled on
His shining helmet and his mighty shield,
And drawing near, cried out, "Ah, wretched fool!
I did not kill the Red Cross Knight! He lent
His arms to one who learned
Soon enough to regret that bold disguise!
Take up your sword and I will show you why!"

With that, the two began to thunder blows
Down on each other, piercing plate and mail
With furious force, and the red blood ran streaming
Down their sides; but blood was not enough:
Both of the warriors chose to win or die.

Now led by all their clamor Una came
Fearful and anguished to the awful scene;
Sans Loi, seeing her, turned from the doubtful fight
And would have run to capture her again.
But Satyrane prevented him. "For shame!"
He cried, "to hunt the steps of an innocent maid!"

"What, will you risk your life for a lady's sake?"
The Saracen replied, "You must be mad!
Love makes you foolish! Come then, I will carve
Some sense into your lovelorn head!"
And on they fought, more fiercely than before.
But Una was afraid, seeing Sans Loi,
And she fled far away into the wood.

The sly old pilgrim, who was the magician
Archimago in disguise,
Followed rejoicing: now he could betray
The helpless maid at last. But we must wait,
To hear the battle's ending, and her fate.

✌ C A N T O ✌ VII

The knight is made a captive slave
By a giant fierce and huge;
Prince Arthur finds fair Una great-
    ly grieved at this sad news.

What man is there so wise in all the world
That he forever recognizes Right,
Sees through the practiced art of each disguise,
Always knows Truth from Lies?
Duessa was a mistress of her art.
Now that the knight had fled the House of Pride,
She followed forth to seek him far and wide,
Again disguised in fair Fidessa's name.

She went to seek him far and wide
And found him resting in the wood
With all his armor laid aside;
His steed was grazing in the grass,
But he fed on the cooling shade
And bathed his forehead pale and wet
In the breathing wind that gently played
Through trembling leaves, while sweet birds sang
And a bubbling fountain welled and rang.

The witch came near, and now with honeyed,
Now with fretful words complained
That he had left her in a place
So wicked as the House of Pride.
The knight in innocence replied;
He held her in his weary arms,
Spending his strength to comfort her
Until the lady smiled once more.
Then, leaning on a sandy bank,
He drank the streaming water, clear
As crystal, that came bubbling there,
Never suspecting that a spell
Had made the water weak and foul.
Diana, Goddess of the Hunt,
Had punished the nymph who lived within
For laziness: she spoiled the spring
And he who drank there felt his power
And manly force grow dull and dim
Till all his strength and courage left him.

Yet still the knight lay idling by his lady,
Wasting sweet words and kisses carelessly,
When suddenly he heard a dreadful sound,
A bellow that resounded through the wood
So loud that all the earth seemed horror-struck,
And trees shook in the ground.
The Red Cross Knight leapt swiftly to his arms
That lay unready; yet more swiftly came
His fearful and enormous enemy:
A hideous giant, horrible and high,
Whose head stretched up to terrify the sky
While all the ground groaned under him in dread.

Taller than any three tall mortal men
He stood; his mother was the seething earth,
The blustering wind-god was his mighty sire;
A knotty oak-tree was his club and staff.
When the giant spied the Red Cross Knight, he came
In furious haste and heaved a mighty stroke
That would have thundered down a tower of stone.
The knight, disarmed, disgraced,
And now becoming weak in every limb,
Leapt from beneath the blow, and yet so great
Its power was, the very wind it made
Was strong enough to throw the champion down
Stunned on the ground; he lay still as the dead.

Again the giant heaved his mighty hand
And would have battered the fallen knight to dust,
But now Duessa cried:
"O great Orgoglio, greatest man alive!
Let him not die, but let him live a slave
Forever in your power — and take me
To be your dear and love!"
The giant heard; he held the final blow;
She seemed a dainty prize for him to win;
And willingly she came into his arms
While the Red Cross Knight lay in a deadly swoon.
Before he waked, they carried him away
And threw him into a dungeon dark and deep
Down in the castle of Orgoglio;
Nor did the giant pity all his wounds,
Or all his shame and woe.
From that day forth Duessa was his dear;
He gave her gold and royal robes to wear,

He set a splendid crown upon her head,
And, so that people's hearts would learn to dread
Her more, he brought a beast
Out of a dark and filthy den
Where he had kept it hid:
A seven-headed monster with a breast
Of iron. Its blood-soaked back was scaled with brass,
Its eyes shone bright as glass;
All holy things beneath its dirty feet
Were overthrown and trampled in the mud;
And on this beast Duessa proudly rode.

Meantime, the dwarf, who had seen his master fall,
Sadly took up the silver shield and all
The mighty armor that had lain aside

In the hour of great need;
He traveled on, to tell the sorrowful tale:
A valiant knight was now a captive slave.

And he had not been long upon the way
When he met Una, poor unhappy maid,
Fleeing Sans Loi, who still fought Satyrane
Deep in the wood. She saw the spear, the arms,
The silver shield, the sign of the Cross he bore,
And guessed the worst, and fainted dead away.

Tenderly the dwarf drew near,
Wishing that he might die rather than be
The bearer of such tidings to his lady.
He chafed her wrists, and as she waked, she cried,
"O day, hide that bright face in Jove's high house!
Shut up all heaven's windows shining wide!
Earth has not anything to show but woe!
Death — come seal my eyes!"

Three times she swooned, three times the faithful dwarf,
His own heart breaking, helped her back to life;
At last she summoned strength to hear his tale.
He spoke at length, and told her everything:
How Archimago tricked them in disguise,
The sprites, the deadly combat with Sans Foi,
How fair Fidessa won the knight with lies,
The enchanted trees, the perilous House of Pride,
Sans Joi, the spring, the armor laid aside,
The hideous giant horrible and high,
The knight's disgrace, and how, perhaps alive,
Deep in a dungeon he lay languishing.

She listened patiently,
Holding back tears that welled and rose the more
She tried to hold them back: the deeper is love,
The deeper loss is; so she most deeply mourned,
Feeding her sorrow always with fresh tears,
Till rising up, at last she vowed to find
Her knight, be he alive or be he dead.
And so once more they traveled,
Tossed by wintry storms and bitter winds,
High over hills and down the lonely dales,
Through many a wood and many a valley wild.

At last they chanced to meet upon the way
A prince magnificent in bright array;
His shining armor like the glancing light
Of sunbeams glittered; on his baldric bright
As twinkling stars shone many a precious stone,
And in their midst one great gem blazed alone,
Shaped like a lady's head. His mighty blade
Lay in a scabbard curiously made

And carved in ivory. Mother of pearl and gold
Gleamed at the hilt. His helmet bore a bold
Device: a glorious golden dragon dressed
With brilliant plumes that danced upon the crest
Joyous as blossoms brave upon a tree.

His shield was covered close: no man might see
Its brilliancy. It was not made of brass
Or mortal steel; it was a solid mass
Of blazing diamond, hewn perfect and pure

Out of the rock. No spear, however sure
And swift, no magic art, could pierce its might,
And false enchanters perished in its light.
Its power could make men turn to stones, stones fall
To dust, and dust become nothing at all.
Now, if you doubt that such a thing could be,
Remember Merlin and his sorcery!
This was a shield he made, with mighty charms,
When young Prince Arthur first went forth to arms;
Now it hangs in the halls of the Faerie Queene,
Where, if you seek it, it may still be seen.

𝕳 fine young lad rode by the Prince:
His dearly loved squire;
Bearing the royal ebony spear,
He boldly curbed a stubborn steed,
That chafed and champed against the bit,
Frothing it bright with foam.

𝕾o they drew near the lady,
And greeted her with gallant courtesy;
But Una answered mournfully and low,
And soon her manner told the noble Prince
That she held some secret sorrow in her heart.
He said, "Dear lady, tell me all your woe.
Your weary heart is burdened down with pain;
But heavy is the heart that hides its grief;
Good help and counsel may bring sweet relief."

𝕺h," she replied, "such grief cannot be told;
There are no words for it."

"But try to find them," said the gallant knight,
"Where will is strong, the soul is filled with might."

She answered, "But if we tell our grief and still
There is no help? Then we have more to bear:
Then comes Despair!"

Against Despair," he said, "Faith is our shield,
And Reason saves us when the Flesh would yield."

His gracious words of wisdom settled deep
Into her heart, and slowly she began
To speak. She told him of the ancient quest:
The dragon that had wasted all
Her lands these four long years,
Her parents, King and Queen, in thrall,
And how adventurous knights
Had failed to slay the beast: he could be slain
Only by one whose heart was innocent.
So she had gone for aid
To the Faerie kingdom, to Cleopolis,
Where Gloriana, Queene of Faerie Land,
Held court. By fortune fair,
An untried knight was there,
A warrior who had never been to war.
His hands were still unstained by guilty blood;

His might was great, his heart was pure and good.
And so the Red Cross Knight
Had come to serve her. But the enemy,
After great deeds had fairly been begun,
Tricked him with sprites and foul disguise,
Captured his heart, and sent his body to
The deadly dungeons of Orgoglio.

This is the cause,'' she told him, ''of my tears.
And yet I love this noble knight so well
That all my woe is more than I can tell.''

Prince Arthur gave her comfort; then he spoke:
''Surely, my lady, you have cause to weep.
At such distress the stoutest heart would quake.
But be of good cheer! For I will not forsake
You from this time till I have saved your knight.''

His generous words brought hope to Una's heart;
And forth she went, Prince Arthur at her side,
With the faithful dwarf to guide.

❦ CANTO ❦ VIII

Prince Arthur goes to save the knight
And serve the lady fair;
He slays the giant, wounds the beast,
And strips Duessa bare.

So many perils stand about a man
Who would be good and true,
Such perils tempt him, were it not for heaven's
Loving comfort and redeeming grace,
We would fall daily into pride and sin.
But Truth herself, like Una, constant and fair,
Forever comes to heal us in her light;
So Una, lady of Truth and loving Grace,
Came journeying forth to save the Red Cross Knight.

And on they traveled, till at last they came
To a castle strong and high.
There the dwarf cried, "Lo, this is the place
In which our noble lord lies languishing!
Now, my dear sir, try all your might for him!"

The Prince dismounted from his lofty steed
And bade the lady stay;
He and his squire marched toward the castle wall,
But found the gates fast shut; no living soul
Was there to heed their call.
Then the young squire took up his golden horn;
He blew it loud and clear,
And this small bugle held such wondrous power
That all the castle trembled in the ground.
Three miles away the terror of that sound
Was heard, and triple echoes
Answered all around. Within the gates
Each lock was broken, every door
Flew open, and the giant in his bower
(Where with Duessa he lay idling)
Leapt up in horror and came rushing forth
With staggering steps and frantic staring eyes
To see who dared to try his dreadful power.

Duessa followed him,
High-mounted on her many-headed beast;
And every head flamed with a tongue of fire,
And every head was crowned upon the crest
And bloody-mouthed from the latest cruel feast.

The royal knight took up his mighty shield.
The giant heaved his monstrous club on high;
He thought to slay his foe in one great stroke;
And down it came like thunder,
Yet more swiftly leapt the wary prince;
He escaped, and the enormous oak sank three yards deep
In groaning earth. Now great Orgoglio

Strove with his club. He could not pull it free.
The Prince attacked him; with one mighty stroke
He lopped the giant's left arm: like a block
It fell to earth; blood gushed
Like a river from a rock
And the giant brayed, a beastly yelling sound
That all the fields and woodlands bellowed back.

When bold Duessa heard and saw the doom
That threatened all her proud and royal state,
She hastened forth, spurring her dreadful beast
To slay the Prince. But now the faithful squire
Leapt to protect his lord.
Courageously he met her with his sword
And body barring the way, nor would he yield
A step to the monster. And so the angry witch
Took an enchanted cup
Full of despair and death
And secret poisons. Mumbling rhymes and charms,
She sprinkled him with horror and with dread
Till all his strength and courage left him.
Then down he fell before the cruel beast;
It seized upon his neck with bloody claws;
He had no power to stir, nor will to rise.

Prince Arthur turned in anguish from the giant
When he saw his well-loved squire brought so low.
He struck the monster on one ugly head
So fiercely that its skull, down to the teeth,
Was torn apart; a sea of blood gushed forth.
It stained Duessa's gay and scarlet gown;
Prince Arthur waded over his shoes in gore.
The monster roared in agony

It thrashed the empty air;
It would have thrown Duessa down
Into the mud and mire,
But now the giant gathered double strength
Into his one remaining arm; he heaved
A blow at the Prince that struck him to the ground,
And pinned him underneath his mighty shield.
But as he fell, the shield, all covered close,
By chance cast off its veil. Now the light
Came blazing forth, brighter than any fire,
Brighter than sunlight. No man could endure
Its brilliancy. The giant's staring eyes
Grew dull and dim; he let his arm fall down;
Softly his weapon sank; and now the beast,
The seven-headed monster, fell stark blind
Before the brilliance of that flashing shield,
And down it tumbled on the bloody field.

Duessa cried, "O help!
Orgoglio, help! Or all of us shall die!"

The giant tried to lift his club once more,
But all his power to hurt and harm was gone.
Prince Arthur whirled his sparkling sword on high,
And lopped the giant's leg off at the knee;
Down he tumbled, as an aged tree
High on a hilltop falls, when steel has pierced
The heartwood, and rolls roaring down the rocks;
Or as a castle pitched with cunning might
Against the sky is slowly undermined
Until it crumbles, with its own proud weight
Pounding the ruin down.

The knight then, leaping quickly to the prey,
Struck off his head; but when the breath had passed
From the giant's body, they saw a wondrous thing:
That huge great carcass dwindled all away
And disappeared. The giant's greed and pride
Had blown him up; when that was gone, he lay
As small and shriveled as an empty bladder.

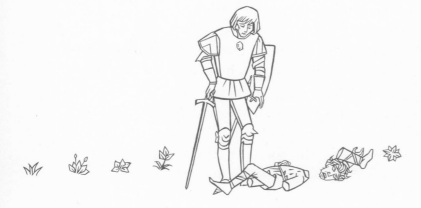

And when Duessa saw the giant die,
She cast her golden crown down on the ground,
Raging, and threw the enchanted cup aside.
She ran away, but soon the light-foot squire
Made her turn back, and brought her to his lord.

Fair Una came to greet the valiant Prince:
"O noble sir," she cried, "most worthy lord,
Flower of chivalry,
And master of the field this day, I pray
Heaven reward you for your gallantry!
God bless you, noble squire, so young and brave,
I have no way to pay you for your pains;
I am only a simple maid, but He
Who sees all things saw this,
And He will not forget!"

Then to the Prince she said,
"Sir, you have won the field this glorious day,
But do not let that wicked woman flee,
I beg you, for it was she,
Duessa, who bewitched my noble lord
Into the dungeon where he lies betrayed!
O hear! How piteously he cries for aid!"

So the Prince turned to his good and faithful squire,
And gave him the wicked witch to guard with care
While he went hastening, his heart afire,
To search the castle. Loudly he began
To call through bower and hall,
But no one came. He saw no living soul;
There reigned a solemn silence over all.

He called and called again.
At last, an old, old man
Holding a bunch of rusty keys
Came slowly creeping out. His eyes
Had failed him long ago;
His beard was white as snow.

And as he crept, though blind,
He always looked behind
And walked ahead with crooked pace;
He was the keeper of this place,
Ignaro named, for he
Was *Blind Stupidity.*

Gently, the Prince asked where
The palace people were.
He did not know, the man replied.
"But where," the Prince asked, "did they hide
Our knight so long ago?"
He said *he did not know.*

Which way may I go in?"
The Prince asked, and again
The old man said *he did not know;*
The angry Prince cried, "Even so,
Prisoners lie below, you know!"
He said *he did not know.*

Calming his wrath, the noble Prince reached forth
And took the keys; they opened every door.
From room to room he went, and everywhere
Was rich display and royal tapestry;

But all the filthy floor was bright with blood
Of murdered men. In every room he looked
And still he could not find the Red Cross Knight.
At last he came upon an iron door
Locked fast; he found no key to open it,
But there was a little iron grate
Set in the door, and so he called
To see if there was anyone alive
Within, to answer him.

He called, and a dreary, hollow, murmuring voice
Replied, "Ah, who comes there to end my life?
Who comes at last to end my misery?
I die a little more with every breath,
And yet I am bound to live in agony!
For three long months I have been underground;
Ah, welcome, death: At last I shall be free!"

A trembling horror chilled the Prince's blood;
Then righteous anger roused him, and he tore
The door of iron down with furious force.
He entered, but his foot could find no floor;
It was a pit as deep and dark as hell.
Yet neither darkness nor the filthy smell
Could stop the Prince (hands that are always clean
Can never give true love and loyalty),
And so at last he found the Red Cross Knight.
Down in the pit he labored long to free

His wasted limbs; but the knight could barely climb
Back to the light again. His sad, dull eyes
Could not endure the brilliance of the sun;
His cheeks were sunken and his brawny arms,
That once split steel and hewed great helmets down,
Had shriveled to the bone. His strength was gone;
And all his flesh shrunk up like withered flowers.

His lady ran to him in hasty joy.
To see him made her happy, but she mourned
To see him wan and wasted. "Dearest sir!
Welcome at last, my knight in joy or woe!
What evil star has frowned upon you so?
Fortune, my enemy, shall pay for this;
She'll bring you three times joy for every woe:
Good grows from evil: you shall find it so!"

Fair lady," said the knight, "the only good
That grows from woe is learning to be wise
And wary of the same mistake again.
Captivity has taught me only this:
There is no happiness for mortal men!"

Take heart," said Arthur, "there your monstrous foe
Lies stretched in death, and lo, the wicked witch
Who was the cause of all your misery
Is in your power now. Shall she live or die?"

To kill her would be wrong," fair Una said.
"But let us take her scarlet robe away
And all her ornaments: then set her free."
And so they stripped away her fine disguise

Until they saw her as she truly was
(And underneath a witch's beauty is
A loathsome creature, foul as her evil soul).
Her crafty head was altogether bald;
Her skin was wrinkled, and her breath was foul;
She had a fox's tail, an eagle's claw,
A scaly scalp and skin, a bear's rough paw,
And more, whose ugliness may not be told,
If we would keep our manners as we should!

The knights stood wondering at the hideous sight.
"Such is the form of Falsehood," Una said.
"Thus Evil looks, stripped of its borrowed light."
Duessa fled away to the wilderness;
Hiding her shame, she lurked in rocks and caves.
But Una and her faithful crew of knights
Stayed in the giant's castle to repair
Their weary powers, and there they found a store
Of all provisions dainty, rich, and rare.

❦ C A N T O ❦ IX

Prince Arthur tells his life and loves;
They become friends, and then
Sir Trevisan flies from Despair;
Our knight escapes his den.

O golden chain of virtue! Men of strength
And noble minds have linked your shining length.
Brave deeds in days of old, and generous aid
To those in need, and friendliness, have made
You beautiful — as now, the Prince's hands
Reached out to save our knight from prisoner's bands.

The weary company had rested well;
The knight was stronger; they could not stay long,
But Una begged the mighty Prince to tell
His tale before they left; it would be wrong
To let him go into the world unknown
And unremembered, after such deeds were done.

Fair maid," replied the Prince, "I cannot say
Who were my parents: when the light of day
First dawned on me, they carried me away
To live with gentle Timon in the wood.

He was a knight of Faerie Land, a good
And noble man, who taught me all he could
Of chivalry. We dwelled amid a scene
Of wondrous beauty, in a valley green
With grass, by a rolling river silver-clean.
And there the great magician Merlin came
To guide my growth. He would not say the name
From whence I sprang, but told me I could claim
A king as father, when the time was due."

Well, sweet young Prince," said Una smiling, "you
Surely were fit for such a tutor's hand.
But what has brought you here to Faerie Land?"

That it is hard for me to understand,"
He answered, "Whether heaven's eternal might
Has led me here to save you from your plight
Or whether the pain that grieves me day and night
Has brought me, I know not."
                                        "Ah Prince, what woe
Is there on earth to make you suffer so?"

Dear maid," he said, "you waken sleeping fire
With asking, but I will answer from the pyre.
Ah Love! Lay down your bow of bright desire!

It was in the freshest flower of my days,
When first my spirit turned to manly ways,
When first the flames of love began to blaze,
The wound was given. Timon instructed me
Many a time of love's sweet misery,
Yet I escaped it, and in my liberty,

I laughed at lovers till the love-god frowned.
But nothing is safe that grows on earthly ground.
The man who trusts his strength is soonest bound
By beauty's chains. Alas for me, rejoicing
I ranged the forest wide one radiant spring
And there I knew love's first sweet dart and sting.

Weary upon the tender grass I lay
And slumbered soft; my spirit stole away;
I dreamed a royal maiden fair as day
Who laid her dainty limbs down pure and mild
Beside me in the wilderness and smiled,
And bade me love her dearly. She beguiled
My soul with gladness all one enchanted night;
Never was heart so ravished with delight
As mine until she left me. But the light
Of morning showed only the grass pressed down
Where she had lain. She said she was the Queene
Of Faeries; that her love was mine alone,
And promised that it would in time be known.
Yet from that day she has not come again,
And I have searched the world for her in vain."

At this, the Prince's face grew pale as smoke;
He fought his grief, till gently Una spoke:
"O happy Queene of Faeries! To have found
Among all men a Prince who will be bound
By honor to defend you from your foes!
Love may be planted often, but it grows
Seldom so great, or on such blessed ground!"
The Red Cross Knight said, "Sir, your rightful place
Will soon be found, and you will gain her grace.
Surely by deeds as great as we have seen,
You have deserved to win the Faerie Queene!"

The sun was rising, and in the shining dawn
They said farewell, for now they must be gone
To new adventure. Arthur gave the knight
A jeweled box brilliant as heavenly light
All set with gold and gorgeous ornament;
The knight gave him a holy testament
Written in golden letters rich and brave;
So friends they parted — Arthur to seek his love,
The Red Cross Knight with Una to the place
Where still the awful dragon ruled her race.

Once more they rode,
But Una's heart was wise;
Her knight, she knew, was far from strong;
She would not have him meet the foe
Until his weary mind and heart were healed.
Slowly they went, but lo!
A knight at arms was riding on the plain
Toward them as swift as if his horse had wings.
What followed him? He stared in fear behind;

As he drew near, they saw his hair upraised
In horror; his wild face was drained of blood;
About his neck he wore a hangman's rope.

They spoke to him, but the knight did not reply.
He stared at them with hollow, stony eyes,
The gaze of someone who had looked on hell
And all the furies with their chains unbound.

At last he spoke:
"For God's dear love, Sir Knight, let me go by!
Look! Look! He is coming after me!"
"No one is there," replied the Red Cross Knight.
"Ah, am I truly safe? Have I escaped?
Am I free of the wretched fiend who would have me die?"

Fear no more," said the Red Cross Knight, "but say
What is the cause of this? Who would have you die?"

Ah, I shall tell you a terrible tale," said he.
"I journeyed in forest with a knight —
Sir Terwin was his name — and a fine and fair
And bold young knight was he, but he loved a lady
Cruel as she was proud; she liked to see
Him suffer, and as we mourned her cruelty,
We met that villain (and from him, God save me!),
That cursed wretch — he calls himself *Despair*.
He greeted us at first, and told us tales
And tidings of adventures strange and rare,
To win our hearts. Then closer, like a snake,
He crept, and told us never again to hope
For joy in life — persuaded us to die —
To me he gave this rope, and to my friend
He lent a rusty knife.
Sir Terwin, woeful lover that he was,
Hating his life and love's old misery,
Plunged the awful blade into his breast —
Opened his aching heart to hasty death —
But I, perhaps more lucky, or afraid,
Escaped. I am half dead with fear of death;
Sir Knight, beware! For if you are not strong,
This man's charmed words will carry your soul away!"

How may a man be won with idle speech?"
Replied the Red Cross Knight. "How can words make
A man destroy the castle of his health?"

Despair has a honeyed tongue,
Dripping sweet words that lull the mind to sleep.
Beware! O do not try his dreadful power!"

But the Red Cross Knight said, "I shall never rest
Till I have tried that traitor's art myself.
Tell me your name, Sir Knight, and guide me, please,
To that same place."
                    "I am called Trevisan,"
He said; "Against my wish I will take you there,
But not for gold or glory will I stay.
I would rather die than see his face again."

They journeyed to a hollow cave,
A dim and gloomy lair,
Dark, doleful, gloomy as a grave;
There lived the wretch *Despair.*

And all about the trees were bare;
They bore no leaf or fruit;
No song of bird was in the air
But the dull owl's hoot.

And there they found him like a brute
Groveling on the ground:
The fiend *Despair,* his tattered suit
All torn and patched and bound

With thorns, and greasy hair around
His hollow, staring eyes.
Beside him lay, without a sound,
One who would never rise.

The knight cried out, "What ghastly prize
Is this, villain, what woe
Have you been witness to, what lies
Have brought our friend so low?"

97

Despair replied, "As well you know,
He wanted death, not life;
Then if a man desires it so,
Should no one lend a knife?

Look! He is happy now. All strife,
All struggle now is ended.
Peace after war, death after life;
He sleeps, and all is mended."

Replied the knight: "When life is ended,
Death is in God's hands.
Until the captain's needs are tended,
The faithful soldier stands."

Then said *Despair* to him, "All ends
In death. Why run away?
More life, more sin. Time only lends
Us leave to go astray.

O sinful man, recall the day
When you lay languishing
Deep in the dungeon! Think, you may
Know worse, with longer living.

And suffer more, and do more wrong,
And injure those who love you;
O life is short, but death is long,
And God in heaven above you

Has seen your sins. You've been untrue;
You left your royal maiden,

You sold yourself in service to
A witch. Your soul is laden

With guilt and misery and sin.
The time is now or never!
Die now; end all your woes and win
Immortal bliss forever!"

The Red Cross Knight was struck with horror.
His spirit all unclean
Betrayed him; he took up a dagger
Swift and sharp and keen.

He trembled like the aspen leaf;
He paled, and stood apart;
His troubled blood stole like a thief
With tidings from the heart

Into his cheeks, first dim, then dark;
He raised the knife at last,
And now that blade so sharp and stark
He plunged toward his breast.

But Una came in furious haste.
"Fie, fie, faint-hearted Knight!"
She cried, "Is this the noble quest?
Is this the glorious fight?

Is this the dragon huge and bright
You promised you would slay?"
She threw the dagger out of sight
And said, "Come, come away,

Poor foolish man, you must not stay
In such a cursed place.
You are not strong enough today
To remember God's sweet grace.

You do not see His shining face
All loving and forgiving;
O He has promised to erase
Your sins among the living.

He blesses you and He will bring
Your spirit into heaven
When it is time; and everything
You mourn will be forgiven."

The knight arose and once again
They went upon their way
But when *Despair,* the crafty villain,
Saw they would not stay,

He hung himself, nor would he pray
Except to die, but he
Must live, though he die every day
Till God's Eternity.

❧ C A N T O ❧ X

Fair Una brings her faithful knight
To the House of Holiness,
Where he is taught Repentance and
The way to Heavenly Bliss.

What is man, that he boasts of fleshly might,
And counts upon the comforts of this earth?
Whenever he must fight
A spiritual foe, he longs to run away.
God helps us to do good rather than ill;
God's grace is all our strength and all our will.

Despair had shown fair Una that the knight
Was far too weak to meet her monstrous foe;
He needed nourishment and loving care,
And so she brought him to
A certain house nearby that was well known
For healing and for helping of the poor,
And all good deeds of sacred love and lore.

This was the ancient House of Holiness.
Dame Celia was the lady kind and wise

Who kept its true unblemished blessedness
Amid a world of falsehood and disguise.
All night she said her prayers and all day
She cared for those who needed her advice
And solace. Therefore Una led the way
To this good place, and with her came the knight.
An aged man, his hair all frosty gray,
Opened the gate, that was kept locked from sight,
And this good watchman was *Humility*.
Beyond a straight and narrow path, the light
Of plain and pleasant courtyards they could see;
But all best things are hardest to begin,
So stooping low, they crept most humbly
Toward those fair halls and to the courts within.
Reverence was there, a squire of gentle birth,
Who spoke to them in courtesy and in
The frank simplicity of honest worth.
He led them to the lady Celia, who
Arose in joy and cried, "O happy earth,
That bears your footsteps, maiden fair and true!
Sir Knight — you are a wondrous sight to see!
Most men travel the broad highway to view
Pride's palaces, but you have come to me!"

Fair Una said, "O lady wise and kind,
Help my good knight and comfort him, for he
Has suffered many a torment of the mind
And body since we came upon our quest;
He needs to hear your wisdom and to find
The way to blessed peace and heavenly rest."
Lo! As they spoke, two lovely maidens came
Linked arm in arm, the elder daughter dressed

In lily white and shining light: her name
Was *Faith*: she smiled for joy and constancy.
Her sister walked in blue, without the same
Sure happiness: her name was *Hope*. Though she
Seemed troubled, still she turned her steadfast eyes
Ever to heaven, where her help would be.
The gentle ladies thought it would be wise
At first to let the knight have food and sleep;
But later, he began to realize
How wasted was his life, how hard and steep
The way ahead, where *Faith* said he must go.
It was sweet *Hope* who helped him then to keep
His courage, when his spirits sank too low.
And *Patience* was the surgeon wise and stern
Who burned away his wounds that he might know
True health and strength, that he might grow and turn
His faltering steps to truth forevermore.
It was a lesson hard and slow to learn,
And sometimes like a lion he would roar

In anguish, thinking of his foolish crime;
Repentance stung him fierce at every sore;
But then at long, long last, there came a time
When he was purified; his soul was free,
And now he could begin the heavenly climb.
Celia's third daughter came: called *Charity,*

To comfort him and help him on the way;
She was the loveliest of all the three,
A woman strong and sweet and good and gay,
Bearing small babes who nestled at her breast
And clung about her neck; (she let them stay
Till they were grown, then sent them from the nest).
Now by the hand she took the Red Cross Knight;
She led him up a thorny path, and lest
He stumble, or his feet stray from the right,
She smoothed his way; they climbed until they came
High on a hill, to a house of heavenly light
Kept for the halt, the weary, and the lame,
By seven men who worked in God's sweet name.

The first was host and helped them all
To share the bounty of the hall;

The second was the one who fed
The hungry poor with wine and bread.

The third gave clothes (not plumes of pride,
But humble cloth, from cold to hide).

The fourth saved prisoners from the deep
(As God saves us, our souls to keep).

The fifth helped any man who lay
In sickness, till his dying day.

The sixth attended those who died
And decked them fair as any bride.

106

The seventh gave the children of
The dead sweet Mercy, Care, and Love.

And their example taught the Red Cross Knight
The way to live in holiness and peace;
They stayed a while, and then with all their might
Climbed higher yet, until they reached a place
Halfway to heaven, where an ancient man
Lived in the constant light of holy bliss.
His name was *Heavenly Contemplation*:
His limbs were frail, his beard was white as snow,
And yet his eyes shone bright. When they had won
His lofty peak, he asked — where would they go?
Why must they interrupt his sacred thought?
Sweet *Charity* replied, "Ah, sir, you know
That one who tries (as every person ought)
To climb so high, to reach the heavenly light,
Must be a man who seeks what you have sought:
The glorious house that glistens fair and bright
With burning stars and ever-living fire:
You keep those keys for *Faith*: now let our knight
See the great house, for such is his desire."

O happy soul," replied the aged man,
"To see what none of earthly dust and mire
Has ever seen alive since time began!
But first a season you must fast and pray;
Then come, and follow me as best you can."
And in good time, they set upon their way
Yet higher by a narrow path along
The mountaintop, till brighter than the day
And fairer far than this poor simple song

Can say, they saw the City of the King,
Blazing with precious stones, built high and strong
With lofty towers uplifted pure and shining
Into the starry spaces of the sky:
And as they gazed, the angels all were singing.

The aged man said, "This is the happy city,
The New Jerusalem, God's resting place
For all His saints throughout eternity."

Till now," replied the knight, "Cleopolis
And the great palace of the Faerie Queene
Seemed of all sights to me most glorious;
But now I judge the best that I have seen
A thing of glass, to this bright angel's tower."

That is true," said the holy, aged man,
"And yet the palaces of earthly power
Are none so fair as hers; and any knight
Who serves that blessed monarch in her hour
Of need wins holy grace in heaven's sight.
And you, sweet prince, shall serve the lady well,
For you shall win a great and glorious fight:
High in the halls of fame your shield shall tell
A tale of wonder. Yet when it is done,
Put off your arms and cleanse yourself and dwell
In peace thereafter. Battles lost or won
Bring guilty blood upon us; war is sin.
Then shall you see that city of the sun
And visit in these angels' towers again,
For you shall be a Saint: your name shall be
Saint George of *Merrie England,* and a sign
To all your countrymen of victory."

Ah sir," replied the Red Cross Knight, "how dare
I dream of glorious deeds — a wretch like me?"

Said the old man: "But victories as fair
Were ever won by men unsure as you:
They suffered too, and thought they did not dare."

But must I put these arms aside, and do
Without my lady's love, so dearly won?"

What need of arms, when love is deep and true?"

O let me not," he cried, "turn back again,
Back to the world, whose joys all fail and fade!
But let me end the voyage here begun!"

That may not be, for you have given the maid
Your promise: you must save her from her foe."

Then I will go, but soon return," he said,
"To climb this path once more, from far below.
But please, good father, tell me once again,
Why have you called me English? For I know
Nothing of whence I came, except that men
Have spoken of my strange, enchanted birth."

From Saxon Kings, from time beyond our ken
You spring — from those who won their royal worth
In many a bloody battle for this land.
A royal prince: yet lying in the earth
A ploughman found you, for an elfin planned
To keep you as her own and hid you there,
An infant, stolen away to Faerie Land.
That simple ploughman rescued you: his care
And comfort reared you as a country lad;
He named you George; and you grew strong and fair,
Till in good time your noble courage bade
You seek for arms and chivalry and fame
At Gloriana's court. There you were clad
In these bright arms, and so at last you came
Upon your quest."

"Ah, wise and holy sire,
For teaching me my nation and my name,
For showing me the way to heavenly grace,
How can I thank you?"
And as he said this,
The knight looked down: so dazzled were his eyes
From gazing on the cities of the sky,
His feeble senses showed him all things dark.

At last he found his way
Down to the ancient House of Holiness
With Una; there they paused a time to rest;
And now the time had come: now he must fight
Against that dragon terrible and bright.

❧ C A N T O ❧ XI

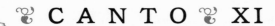

The knight with that old Dragon fights
Two days and then we see
him rise upon the third to gain
A glorious victory.

And now the knight was riding swiftly on the plain
Toward the wasted kingdom where the Foul Fiend dwelled;
And lovely beside him rode his fair lady;
The dreadful enemy awaited them: the dragon
Dangerous and frightful to behold.

O dearest Knight," said Una, "dearest in all the world,
Heaven sees your danger in this hour, and heaven knows
What you have undertaken for my sake.
Only be ready now; and you will win a glory
Greater than any man has ever known."

Then pointing, she cried, "Lo! Here is the place!
Here the fiend is roaming! There is the tower!
There is the watchman high on the castle walls
Guarding my parents!
They are hidden away within —

O how I wish that I could tell them
Who comes to the rescue —"

But then they heard a hideous, roaring sound
That filled the air with terror;
And there lay the dragon, stretching in the sun
On the side of a great hill, looking himself
Like a great hill. And when he saw the gleam
Of armor and the great silver shield
That cast to the sky a light and airy blaze,
He roused himself happily, and hastened down to the kill.

The knight sent Una to a safer place
Where she might watch. The dreadful beast drew near,
Half flying and half footing in his haste,
Beating the air about him with his wings,
Shedding a shadow wide
As mountains cast onto a valley floor.
His body, all swollen
With poison, wrath, and pride,
Was armed in scales of brass
No sword or spear might pierce;
His huge, long tail was spread
In tangled knots, wound in a hundred folds,
Spotted with black and red;
It swept the land six hundred yards behind.
His wings were huge as sails;
His cruel claws, sharper than any steel,
Killed what they touched, and thrust into the jaws
The bloody morsels; ranks of iron teeth
Devoured the rest, and smoke
Poured from his awful throat;
His eyes glared forth like fires set deep within his head.

The Red Cross Knight began to quake with fear;
Closer the monster came
Shaking the scales down tight upon his back
With a noise like clashing armor;
The knight now set his spear
In deadly aim; with all his might,
He charged.

The blow glanced off that powerful hide of brass;
The monster's tail swung out,
Crushing both horse and knight
Down to the dust.
Swiftly they rose once more
And charged again. Though no spear's point
Could pierce that brazen armor, still the beast
Roused in a rage, for never in his life
Had any warrior struck him thus before.
He beat his heavy wings down on the yielding air
Till he began to rise, unevenly and slow,
Swaying from side to side,
Then stooped and snatched both horse and man away
Into the sky.
As a hawk above the plain
Pounces upon its prey,
Then finds it awkward, heavier than it had guessed,
So now the awful beast
Swung faltering, and lumbered down to land.
Quickly the Red Cross Knight,
Reaching beneath one wing,
Thrust with his fierce lance, and the monster roared.
He roared like the raging seas when wintry storms
Pound on the waves and beat the ragged shores;

Black blood poured forth and drowned the land around.
O bitter was his rage: he spouted flames
Forth from his nostrils, tossed his hideous tail,
And wrapped the warrior's horse tight in his coils.

The knight was thrown; now standing on the ground
With sword alone, he must try to attack;
But flames on every side
Licked at his armor and began to sear
The tender flesh within.
The armor that protected him now seemed
Fit for a fiery tomb; faint, weary, sore,
Dismayed, half burned alive, he longed to die.
But Death can only come in God's own time,
And so it happened that at last he fell,
Struck by the dragon, near an ancient spring:
The sacred waters of a Living Well.
The dragon clapped his wings and flew away,
Thinking the knight lay dead; but then the cool
And healing waters of that silver flood
Began their wondrous work; and evening fell,
And golden Phoebus sank his fiery face
Into the ocean, where his weary steeds
Drank deep, and all the earth lay calm and still.

The day was spent and now came drowsy night,
And sadly Una lay for weariness
Down in the dark, and prayed, and mourned her loss.
The night was long, for it was full of tears;
She could not rest, but waited for the light.

The light dawned early, and the gentle maid
Opened her eyes in wonder — for her knight

Arose, fresh as a phoenix from the pyre,
Glittering in the plumes of newborn might.
The dragon was astonished at the sight,
And asked himself, "Can this man be the same
I fought and vanquished? Or has another come
To battle in his place?"
He had not long to wonder, for the knight
Advanced, whirling his bright and burning blade
On high; he struck the beast full on the skull;
And now that sharper steel

Sank deep, for it had hardened in the spring;
And now his stronger hands could do their work,
Because the holy waters of the well
Had saved his soul from every power and spell.

The beast was wild with rage and grief;
He roared like a hundred hungry lions,
He flung his stinging tail
Straight through the good knight's shield.
He seized his shoulder fast

And stung it sore and deep.
The knight could not fight free;
He suffered grievously,
Yet was his honor more
Than any smart or sore,
And so he managed to unloose his sword
And then he hewed the dragon's floundering tail
Joint after joint: five joints he hewed away
Till nothing but the stump of it remained.

heart cannot think what outrage and what cries
The Foul Fiend now howled forth into the skies!

He breathed vile smoke and spit forth flashing fire;
He leapt upon the knight, wild for revenge,
And tried to snatch away the sun-bright shield.
Gripped in his paws he held it, and the knight
Grappled with him, then heaved down double blows
Heavy as hammers, first this side, then that,
Till sparks, like the fire from a forge,
Flew in the air. The dragon would not yield,
And so at last he lopped off one great paw;
It fell to earth, still clinging to the shield.

And now the furnace in the dragon's throat
Threw forth huge flames that dimmed the heavens' light,
And all the earth was dark with smoke and fire
As if a great volcano had burst forth
Hurling huge rocks and ragged mountain ribs
Down in the valleys; stench and clouds and heat
Poured through the air; the knight stepped gasping back,
And stumbled. Down he fell into the mire,
Weary and faint, ashamed, and terrified.

But lo! This day it happened that he fell
(For God would have it so)
Into a soil where wondrous blessings grow.
Beside him stood the glorious Tree of Life
Laden with fruit and apples rosy red:
Great tree that pure and generous Nature made
To grow in Eden's garden long ago.
And from that tree flowed forth, as from a well,
A balm sweeter than rain,
Easing all grief and pain,
That gave life everlasting to the dead.

120

Once more the knight was saved; the evil beast
Dared not come near this place, for he was made
Of all things hating life and health and joy.
He flew away (for now the day was spent)
Into the drowsy shadows of the night;
But the warrior lay in a dream of deep delight.

And sadly Una prayed, and watched, and mourned;
The night was long, for it was full of tears;
She could not rest, but waited for the light.

The joyous day bloomed early in the east,
And fair Aurora, goddess of the dawn,
Rose from her dewy bed
And lightly tossed her glittering golden head
To chase away the shadows of the dark;
Merrily, blithely, sang the mounting lark.

Up rose the knight, and to his sun-bright arms
All healed of every hurt and every wound.
The monster waited early by his foe,
And, seeing him arise, shuddered in fear.
What manner of man was this? With gaping mouth
He leapt upon the knight, hoping at last
To swallow him entirely into that vast
And fiery cavern — but the knight attacked
The open jaw; his sword pierced swift and deep;
When he leapt back, the lifeblood of the beast
Poured after him in a dark and smoking flood.

And down the dragon fell; his life sighed forth,
Dissolving into steam and thundering mists;
And down he fell, until the feeble earth

Groaned in dismay to bear so great a load.
And down he fell, as a high rocky cliff
Whose false foundations waves have washed away
Falls roaring down and pounds upon the rocks
Beside the mighty ocean; down he fell,
And like a huge, heaped mountain, there he lay.

Even the knight himself was trembling,
It was so great and terrible a sight.
And his dear lady, who had watched it all,
Dared not come near at first, but then she saw
That the great beast lay still; the thing was done,
The knight was safe; the victory was won.

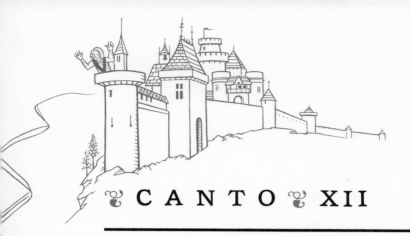

♈ C A N T O ♈ XII

The knight has won fair Una's hand;
They are betrothed in joy;
Though false Duessa tries once more
To threaten and annoy.

Behold! I see the harbor near at hand
Where we must pause and let our captain sleep;
Trim the great sails and turn toward the land:
A quiet bay awaits us, that will keep
Us safe from storms in waters still and deep.
There our fair maiden must bid us farewell;
Her way was long; the waves were high and steep;
And there this weary ship must stay until
Bright weather comes, and the cry of the wind's will.

The sun had not yet risen in the east
When in the glowing dawn the last dark smoke
Rose steaming from the body of the beast.
High on the castle wall
The watchman cried out to his King and Queen
To tell how he had seen the dragon fall.
And they arose in joy, and both looked out
To see if it was true; indeed, it was.

"Open the gates!" the King cried, "and declare
Peace and rejoicing now throughout the land!"
Triumphant trumpets sounded from on high
That sent to heaven the echoing report
Of their new joy and happy victory.
And all the people came
Trooping and cheering from the royal fort
Where they had stayed so long in grief and fear.

Forth came the aged King and his old Queen
In robes of simple grandeur; and their peers
Beside them grave and mild
In solemn garments; then a handsome band
Of tall young men, all able to bear arms,
But bearing laurel branches now to show
That peace had come to bless the happy land.
And after them came maidens in a row

All decked with garlands; and they danced for joy
Sweet as the dawning day
Down in the meadow when the early dew
Shines on the grass. Beside them came a flock
Of merry children tumbling to and fro,
Laughing and singing in their great delight.
They came to Una; the lovely maiden stood
As fair Diana in the shady wood
Watches her nymphs at play, smiling and glad.
They thanked her humbly, and then, half in jest,
Half solemnly, they crowned her head with leaves:
Now she appeared the princess that she was.

And after all of these, the common folk
Came pouring forth, packed in a motley crowd,
Jostling each other so that they could see
The Red Cross Knight: they gazed at him and gaped
In wonder: he was the hero of the hour.
But when they came near to the awful beast,
That stretched upon the ground at monstrous length,
All were afraid; some shrieked and ran away,
Some proudly hid their fright;
One man who wished to seem
Wiser than all the rest said: "do not touch!
The dragon might be still somewhat alive! —
Or there might be a nest of dragonettes
Inside him!" One man cried, "O look! O see!
The fire still glitters in his evil eye!"
Another, "See! His eyes are moving still!"

A little child came running up and played
Happily with the dragon's paws until

His mother screamed at him to come away.
To all her friends she said, "Well, who can tell?
Those claws might cut or scratch his little hand!"
And now a bolder group came close to find
The dragon's measurements: they paced him off
To see how many acres of the land
He covered as he lay; and all around
The monster's body stood the murmuring crowd.

The ancient King came forth to greet the knight,
Bearing him royal gifts, and giving thanks
A thousand times for his courageous deed;
And when he saw his daughter,
Dearly he held her close and kissed her face
A thousand times in joy and gratitude.

And then with drums and trumpets and with bells
Back to the palace all the people trooped,
Singing for joy. The royal family held
A banquet fitting for the happy day.
No vanity or pride was in this place;
For in those times, and in such palaces,
True kings and queens lived in simplicity,
Desiring Beauty that was bare and plain;
Only in recent times have men become
Puffed up with pride, luxurious and vain.
And when their thirst was quenched, their hunger eased,
The King requested that the Red Cross Knight
Tell from the start the perils strange and sad
That he had met upon his wandering way.
He told them all: now solemn and now glad,
They listened to the end, and the salt tears

Were wet upon their faces. When he heard
How tossed upon the luckless seas of Fate
The knight had been, the old King said, "Dear son,
The evils you have borne have been so great,
My heart is full; but since you have come safe
Through seas of danger to this quiet shore,
Now let us plan to have you stay with us
And live in peace and ease forevermore."

Ah, dearest lord!" replied the knight, "so soon
I may not rest, for I have firmly sworn
Six years of service to the Faerie Queene,
And I am bound to fight against her foes
Until that time is past."

                "Then be it so,"
The King said, "For a promise must be kept.
But we shall wait, and when you come again,
Then shall my daughter Una be your bride.
For it has been proclaimed throughout the land
That he who killed the beast
Should be rewarded thus. Behold! I yield
Now by the laws of noble chivalry
To you my kingdom and my daughter's hand!"

He called his daughter forth — his only heir —
His dearest only child, and Una came
Solemn and shining as the morning star,
Bright as the dawning day,
Fresh as the flowers of May;
Her mournful mantle she had put away
And now she wore a garment lily white;
Silver and silk it seemed, and yet no thread

Was woven there: it was a gown of light.
Her wondrous beauty shone
Like nothing earthly born;
These ragged rhymes can never tell how bright
She blazed — and even her own beloved knight
Paused in amazement at the celestial sight.

So bright she blazed, and moved toward the throne
Where she bowed humbly to her lord and King
(Gracious of soul as she was fair of face)
And he began to say —
                    But then before
The King could speak, there came a messenger
Running in haste, and pushing through the crowd.

All in the hall stood stricken with surprise:
What was the meaning of this unruly sight?
Down fell the messenger, kissed the King's foot,
Then thrust before him letters he had brought.
These the King opened; then he read aloud:

To thee, most mighty King
Of Eden I sadly write:
Fidessa is my name,
An emperor's only child.

In helpless misery
I wander the lonely world,
For lack of that same knight
Who stands before your court.
This knight has loved me long
And promised me his hand,
Before he took another
Love in another land.
Now will he wed your daughter?
Beware, O King, beware!
By every sacred alter,
By Truth's undying fire,
By every oath he swore
To me, I am his love,
And he is mine forever,
I swear by Heaven above!
But Truth will find a friend
If Truth be injured so!
            — Neither your friend nor foe.
                                    Fidessa.

W|hat is the meaning of these idle threats
And bloody vows? What truths? What sacred altars?
What love is this?" the King cried. "I know not
What woman says these things, but good Sir Knight,
If you have been at fault, pray tell us of
Your former promise and your former love!"
The Red Cross Knight replied: "My lord, my King,
Do not be troubled, do not be dismayed
By these false words, for I have not betrayed
The woman. Only, in my wandering
That was so long, so perilous, so strange

131

(There was not time to tell you everything),
I met Fidessa. That is not her name;
She is the witch Duessa, and she charmed
My soul away, and sent me to my doom
Against a giant, feeble and disarmed."

Then stepping forth, the royal maiden said,
"O pardon me, my King, and let me tell
The treason of this woman. She has led
My knight to danger, and has tried to sell
His soul to Pride. It was she, and only she
Who caused him to be thrown into a well
So dark and deep that he came near to death.
And now it seems that she most villainously
Would try to bring new woe upon his head.
Unmask that messenger, and you shall find
The craftiest man who ever drew a breath!
Dear lord and King, by his ill deed I know
He must be truly Archimago!"
The King was greatly moved. "Capture and bind
That man!" he cried. The guard leapt to obey
And Archimago could not get away.

The crafty wretch was carried off and chained;
Wrong at last failed to triumph over Right
And all was finished: only joy remained.
The King himself kindled the holy light
That promised Una to the Red Cross Knight.
Now might the two be glad at last and gay;
And all the people shared in their delight.
They made great feasts to solemnize the day,
And all around them now, they heard sweet music play.

Music as sweet as angels in the towers
Of heaven singing, music beyond compare
Drifted in every hall and stair; what powers
Had made it, no one knew, but all the air
Was filled with sounds so ravishing and rare
That each man felt his soul stolen away.
And when the knight gazed at his lady fair,
He thought his heart would melt; he could not pray
For greater bliss, having won her heart and hand that day.

And there in full content he long enjoyed
Her glorious presence and sweet company.
No envious wish or jealous thought annoyed
His dear delights: he swam in a happy sea.
Yet in his heart, he knew he was not free,

For long ago the faithful knight had sworn
To go again, in case of victory,
Back to the Faerie Queene, and so forlorn
He left his lovely maid, and she remained to mourn.

Now strike your sailes, yee jolly mariners,
For we be come unto a quiet rode,
Where we must land some of our passengers,
And light this weary vessell of her lode.
Here she a while may make her safe abode,
Till she repaired have her tackles spent,
And wants supplide; and then againe abroad
On the long voiage whereto she is bent:
Well may she speede, and fairely finish her intent.